Candidly Yours . . .

Candidly Yours . . .

John Cherrington

Selected by Dan Cherrington

Farming Press

First published 1989

Copyright © 1989 the Executors of John Cherrington

The author and publisher give thanks for
permission to reproduce the cartoons from
the *Financial Times* and for the photographs
from the Institute of Agricultural History and
Museum of English Rural Life (MERL), University
of Reading, or as otherwise acknowledged.

British Library Cataloguing in Publication Data

Cherrington, John
 Candidly yours —.
 1. Agricultural industries. Biographies
 I. Title II. Cherrington, Dan
 338.7′63′0924

 ISBN 0-85236-200-5

Published by Farming Press Books
4 Friars Courtyard, 32–32 Princes Street
Ipswich IP1 1RJ, United Kingdom

*Distributed in North America
by Diamond Farm Enterprises,
Box 537, Alexandria Bay, NY 13607, USA*

Typeset by Galleon Photosetting, Ipswich
Printed and bound in Great Britain by
Biddles Ltd, Guildford and Kings Lynn

Contents

The Nineteen Seventies

The Nineteen Eighties

Contents

Foreword

Sir Geoffrey Owen

John Cherrington, who died in February 1988, was the best informed and most stimulating writer and broadcaster on agricultural topics. He had the great journalistic virtue of being able to write about farming in a way which would interest, amuse and enlighten even readers who had no practical or professional interest in the business.

Apart from his writing skill and his deep knowledge of the subject, he had the further invaluable advantage of wide international experience. His early years spent working in New Zealand and Argentina gave him a life-long affection for these countries. In addition, despite his vigorous criticism of the European Community's farm policies, he developed a sympathetic interest in the problems and achievements of continental farmers; he was not slow to point out the lessons, in terms of productivity and farming methods, which British farmers could draw from their continental counterparts. During the periodic 'wars' with the French over such issues as lamb exports and apple imports, John Cherrington was a voice of sanity and objectivity, strongly resisting the anti-French sentiments which were being whipped up in the British farming community. He was a fluent French speaker.

There is a well-known tendency for specialist journalists who spend a long time writing about a particular sector to become 'captured' by their industry. This was never true of John Cherrington. He was a fiercely anti-establishment writer, always ready to question and find flaws in the conventional wisdom. Agricultural ministers of both parties and leaders of the National Farmers Union alike felt the sting of his criticism on many occasions. He was his own man, observing the world with an amused, watchful and sometimes cynical eye. Above all, he had a freshness of approach, a curiosity, warmth and vitality which shone through his articles even towards the end of his life, when he was seriously ill with cancer. The collection of articles in this volume illustrates extremely well the wide range of John Cherrington's interests and skills. Readers of the *Financial Times*, in particular, came to appreciate his articles on fishing and other countryside topics at least as much as his regular comments on agriculture.

Candidly Yours . . .

On fishing, as on farming topics, he appealed to fishermen and non-fishermen alike, combining a detailed knowledge of the mechanics of the sport with the ability to convey to the non-expert just why he was devoted to 'an activity in which I stand deep in a cold rushing river stumbling from one boulder to another while waving a rod in the attempt to project feathered hooks called flies in the general direction of a fish. . . . the whole proposition is ridiculous'.

It is a tribute to John Cherrington's qualities as a writer that these articles, though written by a journalist in response to issues and events which were current at the time of writing, have a lasting value as an informed, witty and entertaining commentary on the farming scene over some forty years. Like the best journalism, these articles will be enjoyed and appreciated by readers who may have no recollection of the particular events which provoked them.

FINANCIAL TIMES
London
July 1989

Preface

To select the chapters in this book I had to try to read all that my father had written over more than forty years. The total was somewhere between one and two million words, all meticulously cross-referenced and filed at Tangley by my mother. Most articles are reproduced in their entirety from the original typescript or the published copy. The only changes are of misspelling or (the very occasional) awkward phrasing. There are several pieces by other writers, which are set in a different typeface.

I took on the job as a way of remembering one of the few real friends I've had. When I'd finished I realised just how much I'd always taken him for granted.

He had a unique grasp of the events of his time, and many of the articles are as applicable today as they were when they were written.

Thanks for what you left, Father, but I miss you sorely.

DAN CHERRINGTON
Noss Mayo, Devon
July 1989

For Ronie, the other half of the partnership

The Nineteen Fifties

*The first journal John Cherrington
contributed to regularly was* Country Fair.
*The magazine was aimed at people interested
in the countryside generally rather than
farmers. JOC's articles were meant to keep
the 'green wellies' of the day firmly on the
ground, if not covered in mud!*

A Farmer Chooses a Wife

WHEN, many years ago, I announced my forthcoming marriage, an old and very cynical family friend added to his congratulations the remark that a farmer's wife was the only wife that could be justified economically as well as romantically. In those days, of course, that was largely true—at least as far as I was concerned. Housekeepers and lodgings both cost money in the hungry 'thirties, and a young man in love might be forgiven for imagining that two could live as cheaply as one.

Leaving personal experience out of it, I feel I should be doing a real service to the present generation of young farmers, and those who wish to marry them, if I just set out what are generally held to be the essential qualities in a farmer's wife.

She should be born and brought up in a town and preferably should know very little about farming indeed. This sounds like nonsense but is in reality the key to successful farmwifemanship. My principal objection to wives knowing too much about

1

their husband's business is founded on a lengthy observation of female behaviour. Women are great efficiency experts. They generally insist on perfection in their own homes. In the matters of looking after the children—cooking and keeping the house clean—most wise husbands take good care not to interfere, even when they disagree with the system. But no woman is capable of such forbearance.

A farm is such an accumulation of imperfections and compromises with efficiency that any knowledgeable wife could find plenty to nag about every day of the year. What tired farmer wishes to be reminded, when he comes in exhausted from a long day spent in battling with elements, of the heifers being too long in the wrong field—of the tractor oil he has forgotten to order—of the undoubted fact that he picked up the hay a day too soon and that if the rick is not turned at once it will catch fire?

Even if these suggestions are made in the sweetest of tones and in the most helpful spirit imaginable they grate and jar on the sensitive male nerves. Man, as opposed to woman, is a most sensitive plant and what he wants when he gets in in the evening is oblivion from worries, and to be made to feel his real worth in his life's work by a wife who admires what he is doing, without understanding it at all.

The only time I think that marriage to a farmer's daughter is justified is when a young man, trained and short of capital, wants a farm. Possibly the only sane way for such a man is through marriage to a rich farmer's only daughter. But the price is a high one to pay and any young fellows contemplating this step are well advised to study the lives of those who have done so. They might strike lucky but they might strike on an embryo matriarch.

So much for the farmers' daughters, but what about the lucky girl to whom a farmer proposes—a girl from a town eager for country life, and not just for the hunting? She should have many of the superlative virtues of the manager of a 24-hour cafeteria! In the first place because the only way to keep a man happy through life is to look after the lining of his stomach. (Eating is, after all, the only pleasure that lasts from the cradle to the grave.) But there is another reason for the cafeteria simile. Farmhouse meals are irregular meals, for most good farmers follow the army rule of feeding—i.e., horses, then men, then the officers.

In other words, we come in when the jobs are done and not just because the meals are ready. Who would leave a cow half milked, a sheep half shorn, or a gossip with a neighbour over the fence half told, just because some woman has decided that it is time for a meal? Now a farmer's daughter would know all the answers to this and how to organise regular meals, but at what a cost in male self-determination! The innocent city girl will accept it as a matter of course.

Besides this, the good wife should have other virtues too. She should be able to answer the telephone and take messages accurately, whatever the difficulties; she should be able to deal effectively with all the various nuisances that call at a farm during the day. With the tax collector, with the man who wants the forms filled in (which should have been filled in long ago). With the policeman who wants to see the movement of stock books—also out of date. With the travellers, with the lorry loads of cake and fertiliser and with the lorries that want to load up corn or cattle when no men are in sight.

I don't think a homily of this sort is complete without giving examples from my experience:

I was spending an evening some years ago with a friend—a first-class stockman who was foolish enough to have married a wife who thought she knew as much as he did. When my host was seeing me out his wife called out 'Jack, Maybanks Pride is in the calving box, she's due tonight, you'd better not come to bed until she has finished.' We inspected Maybanks Pride, and any experienced eye could see that calving was many hours or even days off. 'Well, Jack,' I said, 'you had better go to bed, there will be nothing doing here for a long time.' 'John,' he replied, 'I shall sleep more peacefully in this straw with the heifer than with Elsie when she has this sort of notion!'

The other is the direct opposite:

Several of us were in a pub on our way back from a show when in walked a local farmer of national repute. We started farming talk at once and expressed a desire to see his farm one day. 'No time like the present and there's still two hours of daylight,' was his reply. Then he turned to his pupil and said: 'Phone home and say there will be seven to supper at

9.30 pm.' At 11 pm we trooped in to a charming welcome and a most sumptuous meal. Talk of this experience has embittered most of our wives ever since.

In order to further my researches I asked this farmer how he had come to choose this paragon. 'Oh well,' he said, 'I liked the colour of her eyes!'

February 1953   COUNTRY FAIR

Farm Workers

I'VE just been glancing through my first Wages Book, that of 1933. In it I see that my Head Cowman earned 45/-d a week with his cottage and milk, his assistant, a boy of sixteen a £1. For this wage, these two milked 60 cows 14 times a week, with no thought of a day off, except through favour, and had, as a special concession, a week's holiday in a year.

My Carter for 33/-d rose at five every morning to groom and feed his horses so that they would be ready for work at seven, his final chore was a rack of hay between seven and eight at night. For 32/-d a week I engaged a first class general labourer who could build a rick and thatch it, he could thatch a house, lay a hedge, go with the horses if needed and could in every way be called a skilled man. His hours were 52 and he did have a chance of earning some overtime in the summer.

I made no charge for rent or milk, but many farmers did, as they were entitled to, and I've often thought since that our workers must have been men of quite exceptional patience to have put up with such conditions with remarkably little complaint and at the same time to have rendered such first class service.

Of course, at that time, many of the smaller farms and many of the larger ones too were probably taking very little more in actual cash than were the workers. I think the workers understood this and while always demanding higher wages when they could get them, generally made little in the way of organised complaint.

This year there's a demand from the Workers' Union for a minimum wage of £7.0.0d. a week. This is somewhere around the basic wage of a skilled man in industry and I suppose there's no reason why a farm worker should be denied it, when his brother in the town with something like comparable skills can demand it. I know all the arguments about cheaper cottages, big gardens and other perquisites, but they leave me cold. What the average economic animal, human economic animal that is, thinks about chiefly is money and although the townsman might have to pay a £1 a week more for his house, he generally gets a better house and his wife can generally buy from the shops or on the market stalls more cheaply than can the farm worker's wife at her cottage door from the travelling salesman, and in any case does not have to pay anything up to 2/6d in bus fares every time she wants to go to town.

The other argument adduced against a higher wage for farm workers is that of the extra earnings of most of them when compared to the actual minimum wage paid, but these extra earnings are all in return for the services rendered. For special skills, extra hours of work above the statutory 47 and for private bargains between employer and employed, all these operate in exactly the same way in urban industry and as a result you get many employees earning up to double the statutory minimum Trade Union wage.

So in theory then I subscribe to the view that the farm worker should get a statutory minimum wage, fully equivalent to that of a town worker of the same sort of skill. But believing in this theory is one thing and putting into effect is a completely different matter.

But most industrial employment is insulated from the weather. The employee is able to devote the whole of his 40 or 45 hours to actual productive work. On farms the effect of the weather on all but very few jobs makes any sort of application of efficiency standards to labour merely a matter of chance. Every climatic normality or abnormality, frost and snow, rain, sun or wind, can interfere to a greater or lesser degree with the various farming operations and I've heard it said, and I don't disbelieve it, that the weather can cause a 50 per cent loss in efficiency of all agricultural labour.

If this argument's accepted, how then to give the farm

worker monetary equality with his brother in the town, for I think that it's essential that he should have this or else gradually the better man will leave our industry. The most obvious way of relating output to wages is through the payment of a system of piece-work. I do this on my farm in the case of milk. My cowman gets a fixed sum per gallon to milk, feed and generally care for the cows under his charge. He engages his own labour and the more milk he gets the more he earns, the more work he does himself the more he earns, he's extremely satisfied with the result and so am I, because all question of holidays, days off etc., is taken off my shoulders. If he wants a day off he has to pay for it by hiring another man to do his work, the same applies to his fortnight's holiday. But cows are an isolated branch of farming, their production is more or less constant all the year round, and the machinery and the labour applied to them is always employed profitably. To a lesser extent, intensive pigs or poultry could be organised in the same way, but it's when we come to the general run of farming that difficulties arise.

A cowman will have to milk in all weathers, but the ploughman and the other men work on jobs like sacking, mending, woodsplitting etc., when the weather is bad this occupies idle hands but doesn't earn very much, nor for that matter do many of the routine jobs on the farm. I long ago decided that a man with a hand tool, a prong, a slasher, a hoe or a spade was out of place and uneconomic on my farm but I haven't yet been able to dispense with them. But if we're going to have to pay higher wages, as I'm sure we shall, and at the same time reduce our costs to accept lower prices, another conclusion that's pretty well foregone, I think we shall have to take very strong action indeed to see that our £7 a week is money well spent.

I know that in the Eastern Counties and other intensively farmed districts piecework is almost universal but that piecework is usually associated with casual labour. Where I live there's practically no casual farm labour and I would like to be able to devise a system of piecework for my arable operations. To give my tractor gang a fixed sum per acre per year to do all my cultivating, harvesting operations, once they'd done that their time could be their own, or they could work for me on an hourly rate. I'm sure that by such a system I could both pay a good wage and dispense with a good deal of redundant labour which is only employed profitably for a very short time of the year, notably at sowing and harvest time.

In New Zealand, Australia and America, countries where labour costs are very high, the problem has been solved in two ways, one by a ruthless scrapping of inessentials and secondly by an enormous increase in the number of operations done by contract or piecework. As an example, perhaps a far-fetched one, I read an account in a New Zealand Paper of the easy life of a farmer there who had his cows milked by contract, his fertilisers spread by contract, his sheep shorn by contract, his fencing done by contract—and so on.

I should like to see much the same process here. I deplored earlier in this article the possible loss of good workers from the land, I don't think the system I've outlined would lose us the best men, they would be encouraged to stay on to earn really good money, a long way above the £7.0.0d. minimum their Leaders are talking of now. It would mean the loss to the towns of those who couldn't stand the pace, but why worry about that. Our job as farmers is to produce cheap food in great quantity for the town dweller, not to make jobs. The only way we can do so is by producing more cheaply than we have done up to now and the only way in which we can do so and provide the attractions in our industry to entice the best class of man to remain in it, or to enter it, is by some such system as I've outlined above.

April 1954   COUNTRY FAIR

Keepers and Other Bêtes Noires

THIS for most of you is a season of peace, good will and overeating but for the stockfarmers as I have told you before on several occasions it is just hard work with little reward in generally bad weather. So I propose not to pander to your festive tastes but instead to fill these ages with a comprehensive list of my rural hates.

Ever since I lay, a quaking twelve-year-old, in a patch of nettles with my pockets full of pheasants eggs I have hated keepers. I can still see his gaitered legs through the hairy stems and I can still feel my heart thumping, so loud I thought at the time that it must attract his dog.

But the wind was right for me, or the dog was old and lazy, I was not noticed. And gulped my stolen meal of eggs as my grandmother would have taught me had she been able to suck eggs which I am sure she couldn't. My dislike of keepers has lasted from that day. I get all guilty in their presence even if I have a perfect right to be where I am. I am truly humble before them at any shoot to which I go and I feel that many others must feel the same. I speak obsequiously and try and buy their favour with idiotic remarks about the birds or the season or with extravagant tips.

As a tenant farmer I did not have much to do with them as my landlords were generally uninterested in the sporting rights but I have plenty of tenant friends who told me that their farm was run by the keeper. Some keepers probably look after the farmers but for the most part they hate them too and do their best to make trouble between landlord and tenant. Good farming and good game preserving seldom go well together unless the farmer is also a keen shooting man prepared to sow his roots and other crops with one eye on the shooting and to shut his eye to a bit of game damage.

A nasty keeper is like any other nasty officious individual placed in authority without the checks imposed by the country's laws. He wanders around the farm all the time not only watching his game but what the farmer is doing and many are quick to report any deficiencies they may see to make trouble for the tenant. Before the war it is no exaggeration to say that the head keeper had more say in who got turned out of a farm than anyone else but the security under the 1947 Agriculture Act has at least reduced the keeper from a dictator to a nuisance.

Since I became a landowner I have thought of employing a keeper but the first one I interviewed told me that he did not think keepers should do the rabbitting or the ratcatching. This was before the days of myxomatosis and warfarin. I went no further in my quest and manage quite adequately without.

That may have solved my troubles but to avoid friction on other estates I could give one word of advice. Ask the tenant to every shoot over his particular farm, he would soon take an interest in the game and cooperate with the keeper in all respects.

I am no longer bothered by a hunt smashing my fences and letting all the cattle roam to say nothing of treading out my pastures, but I suffered once and having spent some years in the democracy of New Zealand I found great difficulty in allowing this sort of thing without reaching for my shotgun. Still they break their necks in other peoples' wire today and I just gas my foxes.

Then we have the petty dictators who tell you where you may build your new worker's cottage and where you mayn't. One even told a friend of mine that he could not have a bow window on his house because it would spoil the architectural character. My friend who had no intention of building a bow window went home and did so at once and dared the man to come and tear it down. He was actually trying to get consent for a garage at the time.

I think if a man wants to build a house on his own land he should be allowed to do it where and as he pleases. I don't say I approve of ribbon development and little red brick villas but if each one is the fancy of some individual I am all for him having the freedom to build what he likes. After all the present day architects may be considered a most tasteless lot in a few years' time just as many of the Victorians are today. So let me build and let an atom bomb destroy them. After all why build for posterity if posterity is a very doubtful starter.

Then there is the rural do-gooder. The modern evolution of the lady of the house carrying soup to the poor. The country dwellers seem to be fair game for this sort of tyrant often with some colonial past now spending her declining years in chasing peasants into heaven in the same regimented way in which she pursued the coloured races. Like the coloured races the English villager is too frightened or too polite to argue and so puts up with a constant milking for colonial missions, women's institutes, flower shows and the like when he would much sooner spend his life and his money just quietly minding his own business.

Then there are those who talk of England as their natural heritage and object to fences over footpaths and most farming as being impediments to their enjoyment of it. It's just nonsense. The land belongs to those who own it. Whether their ancestors got it for burning down monasteries, being a monarch's bastards or whether they themselves saved up and bought just as I have managed to do. I don't consider Lord Nuffield's property as my natural heritage and go and picnic on the production line, so why on earth should thirty young people march singing through my fields as they did the other Sunday while we were working and so flimsily clad as to be not indecent but downright ugly.

Another collection of such people recently watched a friend of mine trying to put out a burning field of corn without offering to help at all. All they did was take photographs probably to be captioned 'Wessex Peasants make burnt offering for Harvest Success'.

Then there are the salesmen who call at all the most inconvenient times and try to sell me what I just don't want. I try and treat them as kindly as I can and by now most of them realise that I am no good for a deal but am perhaps good for a chat in midwinter when there is nothing to do. But there are some who come along, the products of some minor public school and who insinuate that I am a fool not to buy their products. This is probably quite true but I don't see why I shouldn't be left to find it out for myself.

Of course high in my list must go the magazine editor who makes me write the Christmas number in August but that of course is another story.

Well I seem to have got a fair bit off my chest so if you are just about to sit down to your Christmas dinner just pause a minute between courses and think of those who make it possible for you to eat them and think of us, especially me, at this season of the year. God bless you.

December 1955   COUNTRY FAIR

Welsh Hill Farming

THE most regrettable characteristic common to successful farmers is that irresistible urge to turn other farmers towards their own way of thinking and acting. This instinct was given a pretty free rein during the days of the War Agricultural Committees, and until recently I had thought it was dead and buried, along with Hitler, rationing and cash sales of eggs at the farmhouse door.

However, the urge persists, and I am pleased to report that some of those who practise it are in danger of considerable defeat. But I had better begin at the beginning.

Some years ago, I was smitten with the idea of a farm in Wales. I must agree that my inclination was considerably fortified by the thought of endless days of free fishing in the depths of the mountains, while my staff in Hampshire sweated out their hearts harvesting, sowing or haymaking, all of them ulcer-producing occupations. I very nearly fell for it, and still more nearly fell for a nice ring-fenced 600 acres on Exmoor with the Exe running through it. However, the credit squeeze saved me from this last folly. But some of my acquaintances, fired with a desire to make something of their lives—I can think of no other reason—are grimly battling to make the Welsh countryside, and what is more, the Welshman, conform to their notions of efficient farming, à la Wilts and Hants.

I like Welshmen myself. I often buy sheep from them, and find them honest; I like their good manners and pleasant smiles, and I like the apple tarts that are invariably served for tea in their farmhouses. I like their attitude to life, their ability to lie in bed in the morning until it pleases them, and their fondness for working late in the evening if the weather is fine.

Welsh hill farmers are sporting of necessity; foxes have to be killed, and although one man could probably run the subscription pack, a lot of his friends and neighbours go with him to keep him company. One Hampshire farmer, so I'm told, motored 150 miles into Wales to see his manager. Owing to a flood, he had to walk the last two miles to his farm, and on his arrival, drenched and shivering, was told that the manager was away hunting, a sport he enjoyed three days a week.

You see, if you buy a hill farm in Wales, you just have to conform to the customs that have governed its operation for longer than anyone can remember. A farm where the sheep graze on the open hill is entirely dependent for efficient working on the neighbours who help to gather and shear the sheep. This all makes for a picturesque bit of local colour. Ten men on ponies, with all their dogs, look fine on the skyline, but they have to be fed. About 40 men are needed to shear a large flock, and they too have to be fed. But that's not all. Your own man has to spend most of the summer helping other neighbours who have helped him, and it's small wonder that things like silage-making and root growing have to be left in the background.

The open hill system makes nonsense of any system of scientific breeding. Unlike ourselves, the thrifty Welshman does not support the pedigree ram breeder to any noticeable extent. His rams are often those that escape the castrator in the Spring; they are loose all the time on the hill, and there is no control against inbreeding and lambing at the most unsuitable times. All very frustrating to the efficient farmer who wants to make something better of his stock. He might buy the best of rams, but unless he is prepared to put his ewes into a private paddock for tupping, he might just as well save his money. Either his ewes will be tupped by someone else's ram, or his own expensive beast will move over to someone else's ewes.

Even if you are lucky enough to get hold of a farm where the hill is fenced, and you have some control of operations, you are not out of the wood. The climate can be, and often is, atrocious. And the land is so unproductive that it is only fit to plant trees on, or run in enormous blocks where one man could own, say, at least 1000 ewes. There might be a small profit in that.

Most of these hill farms are small; too big for one man to work by himself, and yet uneconomic if a boy is employed to help him.

The Government is trying really hard to do something for these farmers. Under the Hill Farming Acts, vast subsidies are being spent. If you maintain breeding cows of the beef breeds in these areas, you get £10 per cow per annum. If you rear her calf to six months old, you get another £8.10s (the rest of us get that as well). Besides, there is £2 for the cow's attestation. £20.10s. per cow per year for maintaining them in the most unsuitable places. One of the commonest sights of the winter on the Welsh border is the convoy of lorries bringing hay at great expense from East Anglia, to feed hungry cows, in new sheds built by the taxpayer, to shelter the cows from the rain that would otherwise wash all the condition out of them. The same rain is also leaching out the subsidised fertilisers and drowning the subsidised sheep.

In spite of all this, the Welsh farmers are leaving their beautiful but desolate valleys. Their farms are either being taken over by acquisitive neighbours or by outsiders; by retired people, by sentimentalists, by people ignorant of the economic facts of life, by the large farmers already mentioned and, most of all, by the Forestry Commission, who have, I think, the answer to the problem here, as in the Highlands. Always providing, of course, that we shall be using timber in 50 years' time.

But full afforestation is far in the future, and I hope to be able to repeat my experience of a few days ago. I motored from home, 150 miles to a friend's farm in mid Wales, stopping only in Hereford at the David Garrick steak bar. There Frank, the chef, will cut and grill you a steak either à la carte, or to your own measure, among the best I have had for years. After that, just enough exercise to work up an appetite for another steak on the return journey. If the day is fine, it's nice to lie in the sun, and if the weather is vile, I can sit in the car and thank the Lord that it's my friend and not I who am pouring money into this bottomless pit.

But his sacrifice is not in vain. I have learnt that Welsh farming is not for me. But I can enjoy its beauties whenever I wish to ask for the ride, and I can eat those steaks with the sure knowledge that no Welsh farming worries will upset my digestion. But there must be a cheaper way of buying steaks.

July 1956 COUNTRY FAIR

Deadstock

SOME years ago I was watching a very young veterinary surgeon injecting a cow with a drug to cure milk fever. As soon as he had withdrawn the needle, the cow got up, made an enormous bound across the yard and fell over dead. The look on the young vet's face was so comically astounded that I burst into roars of laughter. This heartless treatment rather upset him, and he upbraided me for my lack of feeling. My explanation that I was trying to cheer him up after he had done his very best for me fell on deaf ears, and he has never got over my rather lighthearted attitude to farm casualties.

But really it's the only sane approach to livestock farming. Farm stock are heirs to as many ills as humans, though their lives are not generally as long. In any case, the lamb or calf whose birth has been the occasion for devoted duty on the part of the farmer has only a few weeks or months to live before its death goes to swell the farm profit account. That is if the aforesaid devoted attention can keep it alive that long.

So we adopt a rather callous and philosophic attitude towards these happenings, while we do our very best to avoid losses by disease or accident, because these losses are financial. But as a very old farmer said to me when I was starting: 'You can't have livestock without deadstock.' As good a motto as any I know.

Modern science has certainly done wonders in disease control. Contagious abortion, tuberculosis and a whole host of horrid diseases are prevented either by inoculations or by eradication. But we have in their place other troubles which seem to keep the knackermen just as busy collecting our dead, as they ever were. It is ironical that the only disease that hits the headlines, Foot and Mouth, is very limited in its impact thanks to the stringent measures of isolation taken by the Ministry. And it is, in any case, more a debilitating than a fatal disease.

Some of these ailments are the result of high production. The constant drain on the cows' resources caused by heavy milking leads to 'an unbalance in the cow's metabolic structure'. I don't really know what this means, but it sounds well. The effect is sudden and, if neglected, fatal. In some cases, the cow goes into

14

a coma, or has fits, or just falls down dead. The first two can be cured by a prompt injection of a mixture of all the ingredients the shortage of which may be causing the trouble. In many cases recovery is spectacular; the cow gets up and walks away, and does not offend again until the next lactation.

We are advised to feed the cows with minerals and trace elements to make up for these deficiencies, but for some reason just eating these things does not seem to work. There comes a day when you are following all the rules, the feeding stuffs are just as they should be, the grass on analysis is just right, but the animals go down in droves and can only be cured by urgent applications of a hypodermic needle. I have a theory that the cow is rebelling against her appointed task of being just a milking machine, and that possibly a psychiatrist, trained to deal with feminine sulks, would be a better answer.

However, cows are valuable and are attended to daily. Sheep are not so valuable, and don't get anything like the same degree of individual attention. And because in the past they haven't been so profitable, their illnesses have not received as much attention from the research people. But there have been some spectacular achievements.

I can remember picking up quite a sizeable proportion of big single lambs, suddenly dead at a few weeks old. Amateur post mortems would show their stomachs to be full of wool, and naturally we put the death down to wool balls. Now we are given a serum to use against a disease called pulpy kidney; their stomachs are just as full of wool as ever, but they don't die from it. One trouble cured, but I have another, and a very serious problem on my hands.

Instead of farming Welsh sheep on the Welsh hills, as I used to threaten to do, I have a large number of them on my farm in Hampshire. They are cheap to buy and are good mothers, but they have one trouble. They are very prone to die in the spring, a week or two after lambing. This only seems to happen on good land and is a trouble common to all hill sheep, once away from their native Heath. The cause seems to be the usual one of too much production—in this case of milk—brought about by well fertilised pastures. The vets tell us that the illnesses are the same as those that afflict dairy cows, and some other cows suckling their own calves, at the same time of year. The remedies are there for us, and we use them, but still they die. Sheep bred on better country don't seem to suffer in the same way. It is especially annoying in sheep, because it means we have too many orphan lambs about. In my case, I am losing about 8 per cent of these ewes.

April in our countryside must indeed be agreeable, if all you have to do is contemplate the burgeoning spring and listen anxiously for the first cuckoo. But to me, wandering around the lambing field with a hypodermic syringe and a milk bottle, it is anything but a happy month. Most of our stock losses come at this time of year, and you need a pretty sardonic form of philosophy to take them in your stride.

If any of you would like a pet lamb, just ring me up.

April 1957 COUNTRY FAIR

In 1958 JOC was offered a regular column in Farmer and Stock-breeder *under the by-line 'Cordially Yours'. He took up the offer with enthusiasm and for the next two decades said exactly what he thought. Robert Trow-Smith introduced him to* Farmer and Stock-breeder *readers with the following article.*

On JOC

John Cherrington is not a man who bothers much about appearances. The loosely knit, rather shambling, figure— topped by the massive head of untidy hair and the sardonic face—is rarely a credit to his tailor. And the 2,000 acres of rolling Hampshire uplands which he farms, and mostly owns, have many of the gateways closed up by contraptions of sheep wire and stakes.

The hair may be shaggy, but the mind below it is acute: the gates may be unorthodox, but the 30 miles of fencing is sound and stockproof. This concern for the essentials and the neglect of un-essentials like neckties and new paint, has brought JOC a long way.

He was born of professional parents in the year 1909 and educated at one of the smaller public schools—two equally sinister impediments, one might suppose, to an unconventional life which has run from cowpunching in the Argentine to a considerable national repute as a man who refuses to pull his punches when he is expounding his political or his agricultural views.

Exactly what sent him into farming I have never been able to discover: it may be that when he speaks, as he is liable to do, of his longing to cultivate a remote island or to pander to his pastoral soul by moving into one of his more lonely farmhouses in the Hampshire hills, he is speaking no less than the truth. Perhaps.

There are these sentimental traits in the most unlikely, the most realistic of men. In JOC another facet of them may be exposed in his capacity for making friends, and keeping them.

Whatever personal foible or prank of fate it was that first turned JOC's steps down a farm path, it also made sure that the path led to some out-of-the-common people and some faraway places. He even expresses the opinion that most of the men he worked for in his youth were lunatics: by which he probably means that they also flouted the too-easily-accepted conventions and chose to go their own individual ways.

His farm pupilship was served with the late P. G. Holder of Peaton, in the Corvedale of Shropshire. Holder was a man of uncontrolled enterprise: he fruit farmed on a considerable scale, and even bought (but never installed) a branch railway to take his produce into the railhead at Craven Arms, several miles away; and his cowhouse to accommodate 288 milkers won national fame. From him JOC absorbed many lessons, some of them salutory.

One of the great preoccupations of John Cherrington's life has been sheep. It grew upon him at an early age, so much so that he went from Corvedale to Leeds to study wool for eight months, then to New Zealand shepherding for a couple of years, and then for another two years to the Argentine.

His overseas tour coincided with the depression of the late '20s and early '30s; and world-wide financial embarrassment, joined to personal stringency from losing seven jobs in the four years because he always knew better than the boss, caused JOC to have to live 'on the smell of an oily rag' during one of the most impressionable periods of his youth.

This experience taught him to appreciate the problems, the hopes and the hardships of the small farmer in a way few other 2,000-acre men can do.

A psycho-analyst would probably explain after he had been interviewed by JOC, that John Cherrington suffers from—or enjoys—some inhibitory complexes conditioned by his adolescent experiences in agriculture. In plain words, JOC has learnt an invaluable lesson: to steer a middle course between a proliferation of monster cowsheds and private railways, and the starkness of the ranching he practised in the new pastoral countries.

This is vividly expressed in his own farming, which began on 450 acres at West Knoyle in 1933 and has been continued on an ever-increasing acreage around Chute in Wiltshire since 1935. Summarised, it is not to accept the truth of any conventional statement or the necessity of any method or equipment till he has thought it out or tested it or done without it himself.

On the 2,000 acres, 'almost all my own, with the help of the Agricultural Mortgage Corporation,' there are, therefore, no buildings at all for stock, apart from calf pens.

The 90-strong herd—Ayrshires and British Friesians now all home-bred—are milked in a Hosier bail in the field. The 700–750 gallons per cow sold off is fed for entirely off the farm except for a bit of purchased protein; and the milk is extracted on contract at 6d a gallon.

The head cowman is reputed to earn several times the minimum wage; and John Cherrington gets his herd milked more cheaply than most. No cowhouse; and one man can put the 90 cows through the bail in a couple of hours.

In his ewe flock of 1,500, John Cherrington is a realist too. 'Anything cheap and milky—Mashams, the Greyfaces (Blueface x Swaledale and Blackface x Cheviot), Welsh—all is grist to the mill of the Cherrington system which set-stocks in Romney Marsh fashion on some very good grass indeed and turns six or seven lambs fat off each acre of some pastures.

Conventional rotations and grain stores go by the board too, in the 1,200-acre arable department. The barley, 500 to 600 acres of it, is grown year after year; three years' barley, a clover or seeds break, three years' barley, a kale break, and so on *ad infinitum*. The cereal crops are harvested by combine, run through one of the two driers and stored either in bins or vast heaps on the floor of a covered shed.

Investment in fixed equipment at Tangley is unbelievably low, and so is the labour force. There are 15 men on the 2,000 acres, including a bricklayer and a fitter; or one man to every 133 acres. And also Rowan Cherrington junior, of course, the first of the Cherrington quiverful to come out on the farm, after a couple of years' sheep and cattle ranching in Australia.

Now JOC has left him in charge, while he goes round the world, 'to make all the mistakes I made.'

This round-the-world trip is the climax of John Cherrington's refusal to be parochially minded or sited. He began writing in 1943 'because I like the exercise of putting words together': he is one of the men who think most happily with a pen in his hand, and he has discovered the excitement of the process.

He took to stumping Europe for material, wrote about it, applied on his own farm the useful parts of what he found, and got his expenses paid. The result is liable to be exciting for his readers, too.

There are many manifestations of this breadth of interest in the Cherrington make-up: 'I'm most interested in political economy, but people won't read me on it. They only want farming.' I remember a few days spent in Paris with him. It was just as important that we should revisit the Louvre as report together the machinery show.

Recently he has become a personality in the parlour peep-show of the television: 'It's just part of the education of twentieth-century man, to know how to behave in a television studio,' he says in mitigation.

That, of course, is less than half a reason: the other half is that this is another outlet for an acute and restless mind that is always abreast, and often ahead, of the times.

R. TROW-SMITH
February 1958   FARMER AND STOCK-BREEDER

Milking on the Cheap

SINCE I have been farming, my cows have lain out all the year round, and have been milked either in a Hosier bail or in a fixed parlour set on a concrete mustering yard. This of course is one of the benefits of farming in the milder South country. But the fixed bail was a mistake. It combined all the disadvantages of the mobile bail with none of its advantages.

It was clean enough at the actual point of milking, but all the surrounds were turned into an increasingly noisome slough in the winter, and a sort of ridge and furrow that was a pain to walk over when, if ever it did, it dried out in summer. The cows needed far more washing down at milking time than in the moving bail.

If, to save the mess, I drove them to and from the fields by a road, the locals complained. From a strictly legal point of view, a cow has every right to foul a road and her owner is not liable to clean up after her, but if one lives in the country one has to try not to antagonise too many people all at once.

But the biggest trouble of the fixed system was its lack of flexibility; the grazing was limited by the distance a cow could comfortably walk. I never, if I can help it, haul feed to cows, but constant walking, especially on flinty lanes, lames too many cows for comfort.

It is much better to have the cows handy to the feed of the moment, and that, on a farm the size of mine, might be a mile away from the buildings.

The Hosier type of bail is just right for flexibility, but it does have some disadvantages in winter dairying. That is not so much the mess under foot at the time of milking, for the milking shed can easily be strawed down, and on my easy draining sort of land it is not much trouble to get it dry again by simply moving on.

The real trouble is the poaching by the feet of about 70 cows on whatever field they happen to be using. There is some correlation between numbers of cows' feet and pasture damage. Any number of cows up to 30 seems to do little damage, but as soon as that number is exceeded, the damage seems to go up out of all proportion to the actual number of cows.

After completely ruining a number of pastures I tried to make use of what we call in this district 'old field'—a one-year clover ley waiting to be ploughed up, or else a stubble that was about due for a fallow.

It has not been very successful. This last winter we trod a stubble so hard that it has been extremely difficult to plough for kale. The old clover we ploughed rather late and failed to get a good tilth.

So I have been thinking, as I have thought before in these circumstances, of making a change in my arrangements and bringing the bail into some sort of a straw yard for the winter, where the cows can be dry through the bad weather, and so save the damage to my land.

The easiest way to do this would be to take advantage of the building grants and set to work to build a covered yard and parlour system. This I would certainly do if either the grant were 100 per cent or I had a landlord prepared to do the work and charge only about 6 per cent of the cost in added rent.

In this connection I cannot understand the low interest charged by many landlords on improvements. As an owner-occupier I will not make a single improvement unless I can see at least a 25 per cent annual return on my money. This return sounds high, but unless you get your money back quickly on a farm, you never get it back at all.

So cost is the first deterrent. It would cost, so I am informed, at least £70 per cow to put up a reasonable covered yard and parlour and self-feed silage pit. This works out at about £5,000 for the 70 or more cows that I would have in milk. If the grant came to about £1,600 I should still have to find well over £3,000, which on my personal basis of depreciation would cost about £750 a year.

When I have discussed the matter with others it has been pointed out that the expense of the fixed yard is the cost of covering and flooring it. Why not just have an open yard with high sides? My answer to that is that I have never seen one of these open yards that was not either a semi-bottomless pit of wet dung by the end of the winter or a constant devourer of straw.

There is another consideration favourable to the covered yard, and that is the effect of shelter on the consumption of feed.

I find that to keep cows in good order during the winter when lying out, it is essential to feed rather more than the production rations laid down in the textbooks. I think the same would apply to cows in an open yard.

Then there is the question of the disposal of dung. This is no problem at all to those of you who believe in it, but I have been fortunate enough to have farmed quite successfully for 25 years without having dunged a field completely in all that time.

We have occasionally made a bit of dung in a calf pen, but its disposal is always a nuisance. Fortunately there are plenty of keen gardeners around to clear most of it up. But I should have to invest in manure spreaders, front-end loaders and the like, to say nothing of the labour actually on the job, if I were to use manure to any great extent.

I know work study helps in all these tasks, but it is much simpler not to have the work to study in the first place. This would be an added annual cost of £250.

The establishment would have its own silage pit for self-feeding; but there again, it is an inflexible system, as I may not wish to be tied to making all my silage there, and to transport silage any distance while making it costs a lot of money—probably another £250.

To sum up, then, the new system would cost at least £1,200 a year above my present cost. Against that I should have perhaps a little more milk and save a little feed. But this cost would be incurred over a period of four months—a cost per month of £300. Would I get that back from the cows, and make a profit into the bargain, even allowing for a low-yielding barley crop? I am doubtful, and when in doubt the best policy is always to do nothing.

July 1958   FARMER AND STOCK-BREEDER

Food, Smithfield and Christmas

THERE was a time, before the days of refrigeration and winter fodder, when there was a sound excuse for traditional Christmas feasting. The last of the surplus cattle and sheep were slaughtered, as were the poultry, and the meat that could not be eaten fresh was salted down for the lean months of winter and early spring. Only the breeding stock were left alive, and these usually had a very thin time indeed and emerged to the spring grass so emaciated that they could hardly stand.

I don't blame my ancestors at all for guzzling their last portions of fresh meat. In my youth I travelled on ships without refrigerators, and know how distasteful salt beef and salt pork can be. And in New Zealand, in the household of some really economical pioneers, I endured that nadir of all preserved meats, salt mutton. I remember I was once left for some weeks on my own with, for the bulk of my sustenance, a brine tub which had just received a whole sheep. I could, I was told, boil it or stew it and eat the result hot or cold.

The recipe for the preservative had been handed down for generations, and I couldn't help thinking that some vital ingredient was missing. The meat not only tasted bad, it was bad. As a conscientious Englishman, I ate it for a few days, and then a neighbour stopped in for a meal. After a mouthful of my best stew, he choked and asked if it was the best I could do. On learning that it was, he said: 'Let's try it on the dogs—if they'll eat it, it's no good for men.' The dogs ate it fairly well, probably because they were only fed every alternate day, and I killed one of the old sheep reserved for dog meat, and henceforward shared the dog meat with the dogs. An old ewe, fresh, is a great deal better than a lamb in brine.

However, the need for all that sort of thing is passed now, and I can't see any sense in the Christmas gorging period. It is thoroughly uneconomic for one thing, and it can be most destructive to family life. My worst domestic rows occur on Christmas afternoon, when everyone has eaten too much, when no one will help with the washing up, and when all traces of the Christmas spirit have vanished. This hangover lasts a good deal longer than the cold turkey, and can often endure into the early spring. Last year I got out of it by flying off to Australia on Boxing Day, and I was not surprised when a very drunk Aussie at Mascot Airport confided to me that he just couldn't face a family Christmas at his home in the wilds, and always came to Sydney to see his wool broker just before Christmas, and always found it impossible to get back in time. As the plane I caught was full of Australians in a similar state, I gathered that Christmas has no boundaries, but that Australian menfolk could cope with it better than their English counterparts.

Economically there is nothing to be said for it at all. Every farmer, like every manufacturer, knows that the best thing for business is a constant stream of production. Yet millions of pounds are spent rearing hundreds of thousands of turkeys for a Christmas market that might, or might not, be a good one. If it's a good market the farmers do well, and the consumer suffers the high prices. If the trade is bad, which it is at least one year in three, the farmer has a cracking loss and the consumer probably gets very little benefit. Because if there's one thing sacred in this country, it is the retailer's margin.

If on the other hand turkey could be sold every day of the year, as I believe it is in America, costs could be brought down, farmers assured of a regular cycle of production and income, and everything would be nice and tidy all round. There are some people doing this all-the-year-round turkey production, but the market is limited, because most people seem to think that turkey should only be eaten on December 25th.

Then there is the farce of the fatstock shows. No housewife in her senses would buy the beef and mutton that comes from the prize animals. The wonderful carcases the butchers buy at high prices make a fine decoration for their shops, but when the lady comes to buy she insists on all the fat being trimmed off. Yet these same animals have been grossly and uneconomically overfed for months by farmers who get some satisfaction from winning these events.

Even the greatest show of them all, Smithfield, is little more than an exhibition of machinery not in motion, and an excuse for a week's gay life in Town. There are cattle there of course, and many of them of extraordinary fatness. But to win at Smithfield is not difficult, provided you know the ropes. The beasts are not so important as the men behind them.

The first essential is a Scots accent, because there is a legend that only the Scots understand fat cattle. The judges are often Scots as well. As few of the stockbrokers, industrialists, business firms, and other newcomers to the farming scene who go in for this expensive sport are Scots, the only thing to do is to hire a good Scots stockman. Or if the supply of these shows signs of drying up, a good substitute may be found in the Northern Counties. If the stockman proves to be so broad as to be completely unintelligible, and if he thinks of nothing else but pouring feed into ravenous beasts, he will probably produce a prize-winner for his employer. At the same time he will establish such an ascendancy over him, that the latter's only escape from eventual ruin will be for the aforesaid paragon to be tempted away by the promise of more money from some other publicity-seeking tycoon.

Why no one employs a decent, economical Englishman for this job, who would feed to produce beasts of a quality the public really wants, and show a profit as well, I just can't think. I suppose the Christmas canker has eaten so deeply into the otherwise very sensible English character, that no rationalising is possible in this matter. I am, I claim, completely rational about it, but as my doctor says that I shan't be fit to leave these shores until at least next January, I suppose I shall have to endure the worst. 'It won't be as bad as that,' my doctor said. 'You'll be able to enjoy Christmas with your family.'

December 1958   FARMER AND STOCK-BREEDER

Lord Netherthorpe's Retirement

ONE of the advantages of early retirement is that the individual concerned can read and hear the nice things said about him, instead of having to rely on whatever parts of his obituary are wafted beyond the grave. I hope that Lord Netherthorpe is enjoying the compliments paid him, for he undoubtedly deserves the gratitude of all farmers.

I first came across him about 30 years ago when I was at Leeds University. I was playing in a trial rugger match and one of the forwards on the other side, built like a tank, made life for me—and for his own side, too—most unpleasant. He ploughed through the scrum in any direction he thought fit, scattering those who opposed him and those who inadvertently got in his way with a fine impartiality.

I decided there was no room for me in his company, and joined another club.

I often used to think of this when I was on the NFU Council. His tactics there were much the same. Once he had an idea, a policy or a theme, he would carry it through regardless of criticism, with a combination of charm, oratory and a frightening display of his power to sway the Council.

In negotiation he is a master. I have seen him grasp the essentials of a case in a few minutes, and then proceed to batter civil servants with it as though he had been familiar with it for years.

His departure is going to present the Union with a serious problem. Not just the problem of finding a new President; there is no difficulty about that, for the rules of the Union lay down that a President must be elected every year. But of working out a solution as to what that President must be, what powers he is to have, and what is going to be done to prevent too much power getting into the hands of one man again.

I say this with all sincerity, for much as I admire Lord Netherthorpe's great abilities, he made mistakes, and some of those mistakes may cost us dear in the years to come.

I don't blame him at all for making them—no man is infallible—but I do blame the sheep-like Council of the Union for letting him make them. He dominated Council absolutely by the sheer force of his personality, and if that was not enough, he presided over debates by virtue of his office.

It has always been my contention that the chairman of any democratic policy-making body should be impartial in debate. I don't mean by this that opposing speeches were denied a hearing at Council, but once the President had espoused or inspired a cause, he used his great authority to push it through.

His chairmanship of Council was not, and could not be, impartial.

This is a problem common to all semi-political organisations. The great Trade Unions have suffered in full measure from the presence of these supermen; permanent officials like the late Ernest Bevin, Arthur Deakin and so on.

Sometimes they are called secretary, and sometimes President—it makes no matter. By their personalities and by the advantages inherent in continuity of office, they make any opposition to their policies sound almost indecent. So, too, it used to be on the NFU Council.

So I think the first essential is that in future the President of the Union should be an annual appointment and that he should, at Council, be primarily charged with making Council work by acting as a completely impartial chairman.

During my time at Council there were some poorish chairmen of committees and no doubt there are some still. All too frequently when one of these got into difficulties he would be saved by the President's intervention, and often by his taking over responsibility for whatever subject was in dispute. This should not happen again.

But it may be argued that to demote the office of President to one of neutrality would at one blow demolish not only the authority of that office, but also the principle of continuity.

Surely the authority of a President, even a President for one year, is vested by the support he has from the Council? He would speak, I submit, with the greatest authority, in the full knowledge of a united Council behind him. He might not always agree with the decisions taken, but it would be his duty to support them.

Council decisions are seldom the result of a spontaneous debate on the day of the meeting. Much of the work has to go on in the various committees, and the final policy is—or should be—worked out at the General Purposes Committee, composed of all Committee Chairmen, and presided over by the President of the day. Committee Chairmen hold office for a very long time and are men of great experience.

The constitution of the General Purposes Committee should give the Union's policy that continuity which is said to be essential. Once a measure has passed the General Purposes Committee and the Council, the President needs no other authority.

Lord Netherthorpe complains in his letter of resignation that the load of work he had to shoulder was more than he could fairly be asked to bear. That was largely his own fault.

He was omnipotent in the NFU and had he wished to delegate, or been capable of delegating, his authority, there was nothing to stop him doing it.

Council, too, has a heavy responsibility for allowing him to shoulder such a universal burden. No future President should be asked to do as much or allowed to.

I would like to see the authority and prestige of the Union solely in the hands of the Council and elected President, with a permanent staff as anonymous as our civil service.

It is almost certain that we are coming into a very different climate for price negotiations. Until about four years ago the Union was negotiating from strength because of food shortage; since then political considerations have kept us in a reasonable position.

If, after the election, either party has a surplus of members to match the food surpluses abroad, farmers may be in very deep water indeed. I hope the Union with new men and new ideas will be able to meet this challenge.

September 1959   FARMER AND STOCK-BREEDER

Reclaiming Land

IN view of the criticism that the lovers of Forestry have showered upon my head, it might be interesting to set down my experiences of the alternative to planting—the reclamation of land for farming purposes.

I started this before the war on some derelict arable land that I had purchased, which was covered with thorn bushes and alive with rabbits. The thorns came out fairly well from the chalky soil, and then I was advised to use what was called a gyro-tiller to tear out the roots etc. that had been left behind, and so make the land safe for the plough.

This machine, a sort of gigantic egg-whisk, stirred up the soil to a depth of two feet and brought to the surface a good deal of what would have been better left out of sight. Roots, of course, and samples of the enormous flints common in this area. We spent weeks carting them off, and I came to the conclusion that our farming ancestors knew what they were about when they ploughed this shallow land at no great depth.

But by far the worst feature of this tool in my land was the hollow condition it left behind. It was several years before I got it firm enough to guarantee a crop.

The next attempt was some land cleared by the WAEC just

after the war. This was clay and flint with little chalk. Some of it had been pasture in the past, and was covered with thorn and bracken, and the remainder was oak and hazel coppice. I took it over when it had been cleared and ploughed and am still farming it. The lime requirement was high, and so far 15 tons per acre of ground chalk has been applied.

Results so far have been disappointing. The area that had been grazed previously has come to hand without much trouble, now that the balance of known soil requirements has been adjusted. But the part which was under oak and hazel is still very disappointing, and I have noticed the same elsewhere. It seems possible to get eye-spot, take-all, and various other troubles on such land, although there is no known history of corn cultivation on it. I can only suppose that soil in condition for growing hazel etc. needs organisms that are harmful to cereals.

I then tackled a small acreage of beech coppice on a chalk bank. This, cleared of roots and stones and cultivated normally, is coming round quite well, but I should emphasise that this land had all been cultivated at one time, and the beech etc. had only been planted when laying out a park.

Stimulated by this success, I then tackled two areas of cut over woods, which I was encouraged to do by the grants under the Scrub Clearance Scheme. The first one, cleaned with the help of a contractor, was quite straightforward. It was mostly oak and hazel coppice, and though the land was clay and flint, the roots came out quite well. Once cleared it was ploughed, worked down and drilled to barley. This was a mistake. The plough brought up a great mass of stones and roots which damaged the drills and other machines used. It brought up too, except where the soil contained a very high proportion of chalk, a good deal of harsh yellow clay, on which the barley lost plant, and where the gaps were filled with every weed known to me—and some that weren't—although the land had been under wood for the most part ever since records were first started.

The barley was undersown with a ryegrass mixture, and has been of only moderate pasture value so far, partly because of the weed infestation that got well established where the barley was thin.

My most recent operation gave me a chance to profit from my previous failures. I decided that land that had been under wood for hundreds of years could contain little of value to ordinary farm crops. I guessed that the topsoil under the trees might have more value than what the plough turned up, and that if I did not use the plough I should be leaving many roots to rot, and also hiding the stones that smashed up so much of the machinery. In this decision I was helped by the withdrawal of cereal cropping as a condition of the grant. I thought too that if the land under the trees was so poor and acid, it would be better to mix manures and lime with the topsoil, and so concentrate the effect, rather than dilute it over a greater volume of soil through deeper cultivations.

Once cleared the land was cultivated with a tool rather like a thistle bar attached to a heavy cultivator, which cut off the roots left after blowing. The biggest roots and stones were then picked off. All subsequent cultivations were carried out with disc harrows, and when there was enough tilth to bury the seed, 40 lbs of ryegrass and wild white clover cleanings and 6 lbs per acre of rape seed were broadcast, together with a complete manure and, of course, the necessary lime.

Once planted the field was rolled every week for a month with a concrete filled flat roller, and the grass was grazed as soon as there was enough rape showing to provide a bite. Growth was tremendous from the start, even where the tilth seemed to consist of little more than a bed of flints.

The field was planted in June 1957, and carried a cow to the acre for August, September and most of October of that year. The net value of the milk produced, after concentrates, was to the order of £30 an acre. The stocking for the summer of 1958 was 4 ewes and 6 lambs an acre—all the lambs were fat on sale. In 1959 the summer stocking was 3 ewes, 4½ lambs and a half strong yearling beast to the acre. Besides the summer stocking, there was an average winter stocking of at least two ewes to the acre.

Now I am well aware that this high production is partly the result of the wet summers of 1957 and 1958, and of the benefit of the initial vigour of the grass seeds. Some gaps had appeared by the spring of 1959, and to cure this I broadcast 20 lbs of cleanings—mainly ryegrass and wild white clover again. I could see that it had taken root, but since then the drought has kept the pasture pretty brown, and I am not sure how much has survived.

I am satisfied, though, that I have found a technique that will enable me to earn profits on this difficult land, avoiding the use of the plough and renewing the pasture, if necessary, by surface cultivations. One day perhaps the fertility of years of stocking might go deep enough to form a turf that could be ploughed, but at present I mean to leave the roots to rot unseen and the flints to keep out of harm to my tackle.

A final thought on costs. The total cost of this whole operation was about £75 an acre, of which the grant, lime subsidy etc., came to £36. The gross return, in terms of saleable meat and milk and sheep keep over the three years, has come to over £90 an acre. I think the annual production will settle down to about £25 per acre at present prices.

This was the piece of land that was called my 'Folly'. I could do with a bit more of this sort of foolishness.

October 1959   FARMER AND STOCK-BREEDER

Roland Dudley

WELL over 25 years ago I wanted to buy some barley straw and thought I could save money by buying it directly behind the combine. Now the only combine operating anywhere near me belonged to Roland Dudley of Linkenholt Manor. I called to see him and offered him 5/- an acre for the barley straw in several fields, to be swept up and baled in my stationary baler. He agreed to this. Then I had a further request to make, I wondered if he would allow me to put the horse, that worked the horse gear of the elevator that I used to lift the straw into the baler, in a paddock that he had close to the road.

He exploded! Didn't I know that he was running Linkenholt as a stockless farm! What would passers-by think if they saw a carthorse in his paddock! As a compromise he allowed me to use a small paddock well away from prying eyes and as a parting shot he roared, 'And when you go, make sure that you pick up every bit of dung that animal drops and take it home with you!'

Roland Dudley's reaction to my suggestion, sudden, violent and evanescent, is typical. He purchased Linkenholt Manor, at that time some 1,500 acres, in 1924, where he, an engineer in business in London could allow his family to grow up in more natural surroundings. The farm in those days was run by a bailiff on the old four course system, with a flock of Hampshire Down sheep. It's dry, high (running up to 800 ft), stony country, with steep valleys, and in the days that he bought it much of it was under scrub or in a rabbit warren where, one morning, four guns shot just under 1,000 rabbits.

The shooting was good, but the losses on the farm, caused by a combination of old-fashioned methods and low prices, made him let the land away until, in about 1928, his tenant died. Dudley was on holiday in Switzerland at the time, where he met a member of the Indian Civil Service—an agriculturalist—who had been trained in USA. This man told him about the mechanised farming practised there and in particular about the combine harvester. At once Roland Dudley grasped that this was the answer to his problem, an answer that appealed to the engineer in him, reliable machinery to cultivate, to plant and to harvest his grain and, to go with them, the fertilisers which were by this time becoming available to farmers. His reactions were decisive, all the stock, horses, Hampshire Down sheep, were sold, the only remnants the house cows. Making Linkenholt one of the very first of the stockless farms in Hampshire. In fact such was the impression made by his ruthless disposal of livestock that Arthur Street once said that the most miserable end he could imagine for his life would be to hang on Coombe gibbet facing the desolation of Linkenholt.

Once he had attacked the problem of farming as an engineer his enthusiasm knew and still knows no bounds. He built, with the help of an engineering firm, one of the first grain driers to be used in modern English farming. He applied himself to the testing out of new seeds and manurial systems. His farm became the test bed for much of the revolution in farming techniques that spread through Hampshire and Wiltshire in the late '30s. He was one of the first of the pioneers, and those of us who watched and criticised his innovations were not too proud to copy his successes, all the while perhaps feeling more than a little smug about his failures.

This was mean of us, I think, but at the same time perfectly understandable. Like most of my fellow farmers, I was, and still am, hostile to people—industrialists and the like—who buy farms and splash their money about and eventually depart leaving little good behind them.

Roland Dudley, a shining exception to that rule, became a farmer. He spent his money, it's true, but intelligently and with a determination, in which he has succeeded, to make his farming economic.

He became a leader, by his talents, of Hampshire farmers, a member and life Vice-President of the Council of the National Institute of Agricultural Botany, member of the British Standards Association dealing with farm machinery, and a leading member and one-time chairman of the Hampshire Farmers' Union.

When war came he became Vice-Chairman of the War Agricultural Executive Committee and then resigned on a point of principle over a matter that still rumbles on in the minds of some of us older Hampshire farmers. If I honoured him for nothing else I would honour him for the stand he took on that occasion.

Today, the view from Coombe gibbet for anyone unfortunate enough to find himself hanging there would please him, if anything could in that predicament. There's a lot of livestock, pigs, poultry, beef cattle and a flock of sheep. The farm is running on the ley system, and while Mr Dudley isn't absolutely certain that the livestock pay, and he's still uncertain about the dung they leave behind them, these separate enterprises are run, as near as they can be, to being completely commercial.

But this adoption of the ley system is no relapse into conformity. With his manager, Brian Loxton, he is still experimenting and pioneering. He is trying in a big way the use of liquid fertilisers. Every year he tests out new varieties of grain. Manufacturers send him new machines to try out. At 84 he is still, I feel, very much in charge of his farm and very much in the van of progress.

Unfortunately he's had his share, more than his share,

of tragedy. One son died at school, the other was killed in the war, and eventually Linkenholt will have to be sold, but I do hope that for many years to come Roland Dudley will still be there, directing its operations from his Land Rover, still as keenly interested in practical details and in farming politics as ever, spending his money so that others can learn from his successes and from his mistakes.

November 1959   FARMER AND STOCK-BREEDER

The Nineteen Sixties

*JOC really sharpened his pen for the '60s.
He saw farming problems in the simplest
terms and was never afraid to state his own
controversial views.*

Dying on the Cheap

SUPPOSE you were a rich man in the city, and by rich I mean
with wealth running into hundreds of thousands. There are
a great many such in these days of easy fortunes on the Stock
Exchange. Suppose, too, that you had just suffered the first
warnings of coronary thrombosis. Your doctor would talk to
you man to man.

He would tell you of the strains that captaining industry,
or playing the markets, puts on the human body. You take
the hint. You think of your wife and family. How will they
keep the wolf from the door when death, and the Chancellor,
have removed from them the source and the substance of their
present wealth. The monstrous incidence of death duties is
inescapable. But is it?

It need not be so long as you consult the right lawyers, the
right accountants. You do consult the right people.

And in some city office you are told that the first thing you
must do is invest a substantial sum, say £100,000, in agricultural
land.

You shudder. All your life you have heard that farming is
a money-losing proposition. A pleasant set off against income

35

for the rich, but no game at all for widows and orphans.

Your mind is swiftly set at rest. Agricultural land, whether farmed by you, or let, is relieved of death duties to the extent of 45 per cent. The operation is simple in the extreme. An agent is told to invest on your behalf, the required sum in land, any land, as long as it qualifies by being agricultural.

The question of value hardly enters into it because the benefits of the death duty relief can compensate for any minor variation in values. You die. And after what may be called a most indecent interval, just time enough for probate, the land is sold, and your successors benefit to the full in cash, by a measure that was designed for a very different purpose.

There is no risk at all in this and there is at present a long queue of people waiting to invest in land for this purpose. I heard the other day of an estate that was sold five times in the last seven years. On each occasion someone mulcted the Treasury of a considerable sum and made a capital profit into the bargain. It's all perfectly legal.

The intentions behind this statute were, as they so often are, admirable. It was in the days of the Labour government. The landlords' lobby (and don't underestimate the landed gentry when it comes to looking after their own interests), put it to the government that British farming, dependent as always on the landlord and tenant system, could not function when landlords were liable to have their estates suddenly halved by death duties which, in those days, applied to them equally with all other citizens.

Landed estates, it was most reasonably argued, could not be subdivided as could estates of stocks and shares. Arbitrary subdivision left the resulting fragments uneconomic, unable to assist in the expansion of British Agriculture.

The Chancellor of the day, I think it was Sir Stafford Cripps, agreed. In any case, landowning over the past half century had been so poor an investment that only the dedicated would indulge in it. The bill was passed and the results very soon became apparent. Not only with the appearance of what might be called the death-bed landlord, but a much more serious consequence too.

This measure has been the major cause of the recent rise in the prices of all land. I heard of a farm sold the other day where the buyer, an agent, had never seen the property for which he was bidding, and the ultimate owner had never seen or heard of it a few days before the auction. Someone had just been told to put a certain sum in land.

This sort of competition makes it impossible either for a young farmer to go in, or an older one to expand. And believe me, if something is not done soon about it, this scandal—for scandal it is—will get worse. Farms and estates are becoming counters in a racket which surely must be stopped.

And stopped it could be, without in any way affecting the genuine landlord, who needs the protection of this concession. If it were made a condition of relief that the estate was held for a period of years, say seven or more after the death of the owner, then it would go a long way towards keeping values within reasonable bounds.

I don't blame the people who are taking advantage of this anomaly. As long as it is legal, good luck to them. But I am pretty certain that if a time limit such as I have suggested were brought in, most of the attractions of land ownership would fade for the city boys.

There would still remain, however, what have been called the Taxloss farmers. Those who set off their farming losses, often deliberately, against their other income. Perfectly legal.

Of course, there is no objection to a farmer having a taxloss factory, or a grocer's shop.

Except that no-one in his senses would run a factory, or a shop, just for fun.

And it is for fun or amenity that most of these taxloss farms are run. I don't see how it would be possible to single out taxloss farms for special treatment and at the same time allow in other fields one business to subsidise another for years, in hopes of eventual profit. It's being done every day.

But let's not lose sight of the fact that these uneconomic, or amenity, farms in our midst do us very little good indeed. It may be claimed that these so-called farmers have benefited us by the buildings they leave behind them, by their contributions to pedigree breeding, and by the general excellence of the farming standards. In certain cases that may be true.

But for every one of these paragons there are dozens who simply waste their land, their labour and their subsidies. By simply waste their land, their labour and their subsidies. By playing at farming as many of them do, they get us all a bad name.

To conclude. The death-bed landowner must be done away with, and the sooner the better. As for the Taxloss farmer, he must, I fear, be endured but not gladly, and recognised for what he is; a parasitic product of high taxation.

February 1960   FARMER AND STOCK-BREEDER

Less Moan—More Think

I AM reminded of the story of the man, who, on being told that a jealous husband had returned unexpectedly and slaughtered both wife and lover, remarked that it might have been worse. On being asked to explain he said that had the husband returned the previous night, he himself would have been a victim. So too with the Price Review. It might have been a good deal worse, and most of us will be able to carry on.

It is not yet time to retire into the dog and stick farming of the depression years; the tendency is bound to be the other way. After all, we have been conditioned over the past twenty years into a high-production state of mind.

The answer, we have been told, to almost any of our difficulties, is to grow better grass, keep more cows per acre, grow more grain per acre and get a higher production per man.

For the most part we have followed that advice, and so successful have we been, that our food production has become an embarrassment to the Government.

We have been specifically told that no more is to be produced, in fact less of almost everything would save the taxpayer money and the Board of Trade a good deal of annoyance. We are left with a limited market, and the prospect of declining unit prices, as our production continues to increase and imports come surging in.

It's nonsense for farmers to talk as if they were being betrayed. They accepted with one dissentient—myself—the

Agriculture Act of 1947, and this specifically limited the guarantees to what was desirable in the nation's interest.

The Government is only holding us to our bargain. Fortunately the harsh realities are being tempered to us by the effect of the 1957 Act, which limits the fall in the rate of subsidy.

Without that protection things could have been much worse.

It is a waste of time pointing out just how cheap and varied food is in this country. The public does not believe this to be true.

As for the statement put out by the NFU about the relative purchasing power of farmers' incomes, falls in the value of money, and so on, it may be true or untrue, but it cuts no ice at all.

What is needed from the NFU is a good deal less moaning, and a lot more constructive thinking.

Thinking for instance, about the implications of our limited market. Take a look at industry. What does the manufacturer do when faced with a limited or saturated market. He has two alternatives. Either to grab a bigger share of that market for himself by aggressive trading or else to combine with the competitors he would otherwise be at war with to share out the market.

Now have a look at milk. A limited market, with an increase of production that looks like continuing. Every increase in production will result in lower prices per gallon all round.

I am quite certain what I am going to do about it. I have been reorganising my dairy over the last two years, rearing all the heifer calves that are dropped, and I hope within the next two years to be producing something like 50 per cent more milk than I did two years ago.

And so I guess will every sensible farmer I know.

It is true that the pool price of milk will fall as we all do the same thing. But it's the only way in which to keep up gross income. The chap who will suffer will be the fellow who does not join in, who keeps his production static.

Quota is a nasty word to many people. But I've said before and I say again, that the only alternative to quotas is an economic jungle where the strongest collar the market, and the weakest go to the wall. I know that a quota system would be restrictionist, and probably unjust to many individuals. But it would ensure that the small man would keep his market and the big expansionist could run his own little pool, selling his surplus at manufacturing prices instead of making all his neighbours subsidise his greed.

The man who voluntarily restricts his own production at the Minister's behest is a fool.

I only use milk as an instance. The same argument applies now, or soon will do, to almost everything else we have to sell.

All the time I have been a member, the NFU has concentrated on the political scene and neglected what I would call the commercial side. There is, it is true, a Commercial Committee that meets in the warren in Knightsbridge. But I never managed to find out what its functions really were.

It certainly did little to protect us from the massive build-up of price maintained requisites that we are forced to buy.

But in justice to the committee, I should add that its late chairman (Mr Rhys Thomas had not, at the time of writing, been re-elected) has been trying to set up purchasing syndicates to buy things at a discount. This move has, I gather, upset the Agricultural Co-operatives who seem to intend at all costs to maintain their own tiny discounts and their own swollen staffs as their principal point of policy.

It's a pity about the Co-ops. By ruthless trading they could do us a lot of good. Instead they rely on what they call service instead of bigger discounts, and expect loyalty to make up the difference.

I would like to see the Union much more commercially minded, much tougher than they have been up to now with our suppliers and customers. After all, we don't owe these people a living. It's up to them to get it out of us if they can.

The Union seems to have little in the way of a policy to meet the situation, except a devotion to the ideal of feeding the hungry peoples, as set out in their recent policy statement. But reliance on this is a very poor prop.

The hungry peoples' problem may be solved by a birth-control pill. What we need is some sort of food-control pill, to regulate the limited market allowed us. Its provision is our own responsibility.

March 1960   FARMER AND STOCK-BREEDER

The Common Market

DO you wish to see the fertile red lands of Devon and the west reverting to scrub or forest? To see the dereliction of the Welsh farming valleys spreading out into the plains? To see the chalk downs of the south reverting to juniper and downland turf and to see the disappearance of all horticulture as we know it? Do you want to see our arable farming concentrated in the really first-class areas of the fens and silts, and the rest of farming consisting of dairying and enormous beef and sheep ranches? Even if it flourished such a step up would take more land, and less labour, than any other forms of farming.

This is a nightmare prospect, but it is no fantasy. It is a logical development, should we ever become full members of the European Common Market, the Six.

The prospect of our joining this organisation is being soft-pedalled at the moment. But I can assure you that behind the scenes there is going on a softening up process, to sweeten the pill for us, should the decision be taken to join. The only official indication of what would happen in that event has been a speech by Mr J. B. Godber to the effect that joining the Six would mean some slight readjustments to British farming. At the time Mr Godber was Parliamentary Secretary to the Ministry of Agriculture.

Soon after making these remarks Mr Godber was transferred to the Foreign Office, to give particular attention to this problem. I can only conclude that he was speaking to a Foreign Office brief, a few days too soon.

What would these adjustments entail? The first and most obvious effect would be an alteration in the means of protection we enjoy at present. A free market, plus deficiency payments, would have to give way to tariff protection. Not against the Six, but against the rest of the world, and this would raise the domestic price of food. Now I don't give a damn about the consumer, or his cost of living, but I do know that higher food prices might bring lower consumption.

An outright casualty would be horticulture. I don't know the value of the Glasshouse business, but once the tariff protection was removed I can't see it even existing against the competition of imports from the Mediterranean. Transport is cheaper than an artificial climate.

Similarly, out-of-door crops, like early potatoes, vegetables and fruit, would be assailed by the produce of sunnier and earlier lands.

The position of pig and poultry keepers would be threatened, not only by the output of cheaper and family labour on Continental farms, but also by a disadvantageous price for feed grains. At the moment farmers in Britain buy the cheapest feed grain in the world, whether imported or home-grown. The change to EEC systems of protection would mean that imported grain would carry a duty designed to support home grain prices.

This would not be the same all round, as in the Six imported feed is only 20 per cent of the total used, as against 40 per cent in Britain.

The grain supports at present proposed for the Six will work something like this. By agreement with farmers a target price is fixed. A support body, the European Grain Bureau, will support the target price by purchases on the market at prices 5 per cent to 7 per cent below the target price. Funds for this operation will be levied by duties on imported grain.

If the prices fixed within the Six are high, then duties will have to be high, an almost certain way of reducing imports and therefore tariff revenue. The only other source of funds open to the Grain Bureau are levies on cereal growers. So in the event of a large crop or a bad market the price would be supported almost entirely by the growers themselves.

I don't think this point has been sufficiently appreciated by the large scale cereal farmers who are inclined to scoff at fears about the Common Market. Target prices in the Six such as £35 per ton for wheat and about £29 for barley look attractive but are not, in fact, being realised by growers. Indeed, there is in France at the moment a surplus of one million tons of barley and 700,000 tons of wheat.

The scope for increased grain production, both in France and North West Germany is, I understand, enormous. And particularly in France the climate and soil conditions make it one of the world's easiest countries in which to mechanise.

Still on the arable side there is sugar beet. There are no

special reasons why this crop should be reserved for British farmers. There is a very large beet surplus on the Continent, especially in France, where at present the surplus beet is made into alcohol.

Is liquid milk bound to be safe? Not a bit of it! Already under the Outer Seven Agreement our cream market is being under-cut from Denmark. Holland, a member of the Six, produces milk-off-grass products a great deal more cheaply than we seem to. And, as I saw in America, there are various methods of reducing the water content of milk so that transport costs can be cut. Milk could be delivered in Britain from Continental farms.

Even beef is not such a certain bet. The planning people in the Six set a figure for beef production for France for 1961. Already that figure is well within sight, a year early. Beef is certainly dearer on the Continent at present than it is in England. But a small surplus could lead to a savage fall in market price, and in any case our pure bred beef is unsuitable for the Continental trade as being too fat.

The sponsors of the Common Market claim that special arrangements will have to be made for British farming on joining. These will be worked out by all interested countries in conference.

What hope would our representatives have in such a set up? There are three hundred thousand farmers in Britain. There are many times that number in the countries making up the Six. Besides which, these countries are already trying to increase food production with a view to gaining export markets. The voting would always be six to one against our farming. Besides which, a market for food in the British Isles, would be the only thing our industrialists could offer the Six in exchange for their own exports.

Do you still think the picture I have drawn of a derelict countryside impossible? That it can't happen here? The United States of America is the greatest common market the world has known to date. There, because of the brutal effect of uncontrolled economic forces, millions of acres are derelict, growing scrub, or just providing exercise ground for cattle. None but the best of the land is cultivated at all.

Just remember that most of Britain consists of difficult

farming land, complicated by an appalling climate. In spite of that, and with the help of some protection, Britain is as well cultivated as most countries in the world and British farming is of undoubted economic advantage to the Nation. As I see it, joining the Six would remove that protection, and could well ruin a great part of our farming. That can't be a good thing, either for us or our countrymen.

December 1960   FARMER AND STOCK-BREEDER

Woolley Quotas

MR Harold Woolley is quoted as saying that the 1961 Price Review was one of the most 'forward looking' for several years. Well, I suppose in his position he has to say something, whether it means anything or nothing. After all he is only following the precedent set by Lord Netherthorpe who, in a spot, used to make a speech so long, so platitudinous and so confused as to batter his critics into apathy.

But Netherthorpe's speeches did at least sound as though they meant something. Woolley's, lacking the fire of the original, just sound woolly.

What does 'forward looking' really mean? Does it mean that the NFU is really looking forward to milk quotas? I went to both the Minister's and Mr Woolley's press conferences, and asked each of them to define what was meant by a 'two-tiered price system that would bring home to the producer just what his surplus milk was fetching.'

When I suggested that Quota was the only word to fit the bill it was as if I had made use of one of those horrid four letter words in public.

Such was the horrified reaction that I gathered that Quota is an obscene word nowadays in Knightsbridge and Whitehall; and I fully expect a summons to appear at the Old Bailey because of my persistent use of it.

But Quota is the word. And I can't understand the NFU

making a bargain for an extra 0.8d per gallon on the understanding that, should no way of making quotas work be agreed, the money could be withdrawn next year.

In any case the money does not really belong to the Government. It has been taken from the housewife by raising the price of summer milk. Will the housewife get it back if we don't conform?

Of course, I have always said publicly that quotas were the answer to our progressive over-production of milk. But I have always considered myself a voice crying in the wilderness, except recently for the Farmers' Union of Wales.

Can it be that NFU policy is now being dictated from Tangley and Aberystwyth?

The NFU has been completely outmanoeuvred. Without a mandate from members it has accepted a principle that recognises the limitation of our milk market and the right of the Government to dictate it. I think a quota system 'forward thinking'; but I don't think Mr Woolley meant quite that.

Then what is there 'forward looking' about the cut in barley prices? Only a small percentage of farmers grow barley for sale. As they are mostly large farmers they are obvious targets for cuts by an organisation controlled by small ones.

In my own case the cut will cost me about £750. If I add my increase in subscription, £70, I feel that Mr Woolley's period of office is proving so disastrously expensive for me that it might be policy to pension him off.

But worse is to come. A scheme for storing barley is in the offing, so that the bad boys who sell at harvest will suffer and the good boys who store will be rewarded.

Who is this all in aid of? Most certainly not the Government, whose aim it is to reduce the subsidy. Barley to-day is worth just about what it was at harvest. No amount of storing will raise the average price one little bit, as long as there is a constant flow of imports of barley and maize to keep down the price.

But it will help the compounder. He likes to use home-grown barley if he can get it cheaper. The leaders of that industry are always calling for a regular flow off the farms; but are always very coy about paying farmers enough to make storing worth while. It would be, they declare, uneconomic for them to pay farmers to store barley.

Someone has taken pity on their straitened circumstances. Some farmers will be paid to store their barley, but the money will be found by other growers.

According to my best-informed spies, the selling season will be divided into three periods. The middle one, probably December–January, will be standard price. The earlier one will take the lowest, the later the highest.

Suppose the standard acreage payment is £10. The harvest seller might get £7 10s—and the storer £12 10s. Nothing less than a spread of £5 would make storage worth while.

But the harvest sellers are not all foolish virgins. They include the malting barley specialists. The malting trade is mostly at harvest these days, so any premium for malting barley may well be nullified by the lower acreage payment.

But that is not all. My same spies tell me that the mechanics of the scheme will be roughly as follows. People who feed all their own barley will be paid the standard rate. People who sell all or part of their crop will have to sell it all or lose the payment. Just like the present wheat scheme.

In other words, if you want to use some of your barley for seed or feed and sell the rest you must sell it all and buy some back again.

The trade, of course, have been after this for years, and now it looks as if they have won. Your only hope, which is one that I share, is that my spies are wrong. But there is nothing very forward looking from our point of view in any of this.

Let us just take a look at the famous offer of half a million pounds for marketing research, which the NFU turned down. It was turned down apparently because the NFU was not ready for it, and the money in any case would have come out of the Price Review award. It must also be said that in the NFU's coffers is no similar sum to match the Government's offer.

But why did Mr Soames make the offer? His own explanation on television was that there was a surplus of food in the western world, trade was becoming more and more competitive, and it was up to British farmers to produce a competitive selling system.

He might have added, but did not, that this competitive market was entirely due to the Government's import policy.

By offering money that was not his, which he knew would

not be accepted, he effectively put the NFU in the wrong and the Government in the right. He's the only forward looker in the party.

April 1961   FARMER AND STOCK-BREEDER

Going Farming?—Don't!

A S my readers will know, my thoughts on starting farming these days are apt to be discouraging. Part of this attitude is, of course, self-protection. I have no intention of being held responsible for anybody's ill-considered venture into farming. But I also feel that the general economic situation, with food surpluses piling up everywhere, is so dangerous that it would be foolish not to take note of it.

I was holding forth on these lines the other day to a young man who had penetrated into my den, when he retaliated with a question as to what things had been really like when I had started. I thought quickly. And then replied that had I not been a fool I should never have started farming at all.

When I left school in 1927, determined to be a farmer, every farmer's son in England with any sense at all was trying to get into something else. I spent four years in New Zealand and South America where farmers were enduring a depression that made the sufferings of English farmers at that time seem very small beer indeed.

I came back to England in 1932 when the fall in prices was at its worst, and took my first farm the next year; and 1933 was probably the cheapest year in which to take a farm. But of course I did not know it at the time.

My established farming neighbours looked on me with considerable pity. They were very kind and helpful, but all their kindness could not conceal the certainty that, in their own minds, I was doomed to lose what capital I had, quickly and miserably. After all, many of them were doing just that, in spite of all their inherited and acquired skill. What chance had a newcomer in such circumstances.

That I succeeded at all was due to the most outrageous luck. By 1935 costs had at last fallen below prices, and prices were beginning to climb off the floor. From then on it has been plain sailing. There was a gentle improvement until the war came, and since then established farmers have had little to complain about, at least those of us who remember those pre-war days.

It's important to remember that I now belong to the ranks of established farmers. My capital has grown with these inflationary times so that I can finance my own operations. The capital that is locked up, at present values, in my land and stock is hardly earning its keep by the standards of the city. And were my business a public company I, in common with many other established farmers, would be subject to the take-over attentions of Mr Clore and his friends.

It is from this comfortable position that I consider the prospects of the ambitious would-be farmer. Like my mentors of other years, I am firmly convinced that any young man who wishes to break into farming to-day must be, as I was, a fool.

But here the similarity ends. At the time I started English farming was in a state of virtual bankruptcy. Prices had fallen so low as to make it almost certain that the next move was almost bound to be upwards. Farmers had seen between 60 and 70 per cent of their capital of ten or 12 years before vanish with the general fall in prices of land, stock and crops.

Now this did not really affect farmers who had been in business for a long time and who had guided their affairs with the caution that experience taught them. But it was disastrous for those who had purchased their farms at high prices or who had come into farming in the early Twenties. Most of these had borrowed the money. And while it is a bad thing to lose one's own money, it is a good deal worse, I always think, to lose someone else's.

This is an apt point at the present time. I think, and so do many others, that the cost of starting a farm to-day is a good deal more than commercial prudence would advise. The value of land is kept at a high level by a variety of causes; scarcity, fear of inflation, death duty relief, desire for amenity and so on.

Should there be any reduction in the intensity of this pressure for land (and quite simple factors could cause this: a bad slump on the Stock Exchange, or an alteration of the present death duty relief of 45 per cent) the result could be a general fall in prices. This could be quite disastrous for men who had borrowed money on a long term to pay present inflated prices.

Now this is cold comfort to the young aspirant to farming. He is left, if my theory is in any way right, with the choice between investing now in the probability of losing a good deal of his capital, while working hard at the same time, or hanging on waiting for a slump that may never happen.

Now the young man who asked me the question in the first place was in no way stupid. He had been to a good school, had worked on a farm for a year or two and followed that by attendance for two years at a well-known agricultural college, where he had acquired the diploma handed out to students who do their work well. He had then worked again on a farm, and was at the time of his visit to me a good hard-working practical man, well qualified to run a farm of his own.

But he had only a small amount of capital; and the realisation of the basic economic facts that I have been describing was beginning to penetrate a mind confused by a traditional agricultural education.

He talked rather bitterly before he left, and this bitterness was directed at those who had fostered his farming education. If he had been acquainted when he left school, or at college, with the real facts of farming, he would have chosen something else, and not wasted six or seven years working up a blind alley.

I think his bitterness was justified.

July 1953   FARMER AND STOCKBREEDER

One Cow One Vote

THE scene is a covered yard between milkings. Various cows are lying about chewing the cud. Enter a young heifer, fresh into the herd that day. She approaches an elderly matron (possibly her mother, but how can she tell?), and speaks:

YOUNG HEIFER: Good morning to you. What a lot of cows there are here to-day.

ELDERLY COW: Yes, aren't there? It's because Farmer Brown has to keep adding to the herd.

YH: Why does he have to do that?

EC: Well, it's because of the Milk Marketing Board.

YH: What is the Milk Marketing Board?

EC coughs and almost swallows her cud the wrong way: It's a Farmer's Organisation that takes our milk from the farm to the factory, and finally bottles it or makes it into butter to sell to the public.

YH: If Farmer Brown keeps adding to his herd because of the Milk Marketing Board is that because the Milk Marketing Board hasn't got enough milk to sell?

EC: On the contrary. The Milk Marketing Board has more milk than it can sell profitably already. Because of that, a lot of milk is sold cheaper for butter-making, and so the price of milk to all dairy farmers like Farmer Brown is steadily dropping. So, in order to pay wages and other expenses and make a profit, Farmer Brown, like all other farmers, must try and keep his gallonage continually rising to make up for his decline in income.

YH: Do all farmers do as Farmer Brown's done?

EC: Dear me, no. Very many farmers have given up keeping cows—something like 50,000 during the past few years. A lot of others whose farms are too small are having to make do on lower and lower incomes. They are not a bit happy about this.

YH: Well why isn't anything done about it?

EC: The Minister of Agriculture, Mr Soames, tried two years ago to persuade farmers to agree to a quota system. This would mean that those who produced more than the market required would have to accept a lower price for their extra milk if they wished to go on producing it. And those who, for various reasons, could not increase their supply would be able to maintain the same income. However, although some Welsh farmers and, it is believed, some English farmers were in favour of this, the Milk Marketing Board turned it down.

YH: But why, if the Board is supposed to be the Farmers' Board, did it not approve of Mr Soames' suggestion? It seems common sense to me.

EC: It is difficult for us bovines to understand the workings of the human mind. The trouble is that although the original intention of those setting up the Board was simply to market farmers' milk, to-day it is concerned with all sorts of other things as well. It has a whole section, perhaps its most productive section, teaching farmers how to produce more milk, and this section is very strong in the councils of the Board.

YH: But surely this production section is only a servant of the Board. Don't farmers control the Board? Couldn't they force the Board to adopt this two-price system?

EC: Ah, that's where democracy comes in. You see, farmers when electing members of a Marketing Board do not just vote themselves. They can add votes according to the number of cows they have. So one farmer with 10 cows has only a tenth of the voting strength of one farmer with 100 cows.

YH: But that's not democracy. I still don't see where democracy comes in.

EC flicked her tail in exasperation: You're too young to understand these things. Let me explain further. The reason there's no acceptance of the quota system is that comparatively few farmers each owning many cows prefer to produce this extra milk, which is subsidised by the many farmers who, for various reasons, cannot increase their output.

YH: Is there anything these smaller farmers can do about it then?

EC: Yes, of course. They could, if they had any sense, combine together and elect members to the Board who were of their way of thinking. But it would be difficult because most of the voting strength, that is most of the cows, are in the hands of a minority of large farmers.

YH: What a horribly unjust thing democracy of this sort is. Someone ought to do something about it.

EC: Tush, tush, my dear. Control those idealistic feelings. You should realise that, under its present set-up, the Milk Marketing Board is controlled by cows, and democracy works extremely well for us. Just fancy, if common sense and logic rather than greed and short-sightedness controlled the Milk Marketing Board, farmers wouldn't need so many cows, and if that happened you, my dear, might well have ended up as barley beef at twelve months old. Instead, you and thousands like you are going to be able to lead perfectly happy natural lives, having calves and giving milk.

YH crossly: I don't call artificial insemination very natural or very enjoyable.

EC: Nor do I, but it's a small price to pay for our privileged position in the world of men.

(They fall quiet. Enter Farmer Brown with voting paper in his hand. He counts the cows, puts the total down and then hurries off to post the form so that yet another anti-quota candidate maintains his seat on the Milk Marketing Board.)

February 1963   FARMER AND STOCKBREEDER

Tom Parker

FARMERS who endured the depression of the 20s and 30s commonly carry the marks of it in their farming. They are cautious men, who never believe the good times we have enjoyed since 1940 will last longer than the next Price Review, or at best the next election. So their farms, while tidy and productive, are run to some extent on a shoe string. Buildings are patched and repaired. Machinery renewed only when necessary, and not according to some tax saving myth. There is no more labour than absolutely necessary.

Tom Parker of Stokewood, Droxford, in Hampshire, is not one of these. Yet he must have had as hard a time as any through those bleak years. The day after he left school at the age of 14 he was driving a team of horses on his Father's farm at Bentworth in East Hampshire. He became head carter and then foreman, and remained with his Father until, on marriage, he took his own farm.

He told me that he had never worked as hard, or as skilfully, as he did in the first three years he was on his own, yet, when he added up his assets at the end of three years, he found he was not one penny the better off. However he persisted, and in the early thirties moved to Charity Farm, Fareham. This was the turning point. Costs by then had reached rock bottom, and prices all through the thirties rose very gradually. He made the most of his surroundings. The land at Fareham is good for vegetables, and soon he was selling these, and milk and eggs, as well in Fareham and in Portsmouth almost next door.

The business prospered, more land was rented or purchased, until to-day he farms, in partnership with members of his family, something like 3,000 acres. Some of it is still the good land of the Fareham district, but some is what I would call the worst of Hampshire. The land around Stokewood is a flinty loam, so full of stone that it's hard to tell a fallow from a gravel road. Taming this land, for that is what his farming really is, brings out all the truculence in his nature. He just won't be beaten. Potatoes and sugar beet are planted, where faint-hearts would prate about wear on machines and misshapen tubers. He farms as if he had the best land in Britain, not some of the worst. He farms with pride. Everything is tidy. Concrete has been poured with a generous hand. His grain and potato storage dominates the rolling Hampshire scene like a minor cathedral. He insists on the job being well done and at the right time, and to make sure of this has never economised on labour. Two sons and a son-in-law are active in management, but he himself is still very much the Governor. He knows what's going on and, I suspect, is still the mainspring.

Like many successful men in farming he strikes a new acquaintance as somewhat bombastic, intolerant of new ideas, especially if put forward by farmers not so good as he. Yet this I have come to think is all part of his technique. His scorn will exact from his victim the fullest defence of whatever is the subject of the argument. Once he has the full facts, Tom will seldom let a good idea escape.

Besides his farming his great joy is horses. He rides daily round the farms, nothing to beat the saddle as a farm office. He has always hunted and is Joint Master of the Hampshire Hunt. Some of his milk is still delivered by horse power, but his great hobby is his coach team. Many of you will have seen them at the Summer Shows with Tom Parker, immaculate in Top Hat and Morning Suit, driving them round the ring on the way to some coaching marathon. Perhaps he gets his greatest satisfaction from this lordly height. He's come a long way from the 14 year old who stumbled along the stony furrows behind his Father's team, but don't be misled by this, his feet are still firmly bedded in Hampshire flints.

October 1963   FARMER AND STOCKBREEDER

JOC started writing for the Financial Times *in the '60s. He never talked down to his City readers—rather he welcomed the chance to give them an honest insight into what farmers preferred to see kept a closed book.*

Factory Farming

IF you were to confine a horse, or a dog, or a cat, in a space so small that it could neither turn round, or stretch itself. Where it had no bedding but wire or slats and where the lack of exercise, and a restricted diet, so weakened its bones and stiffened its joints, that its limbs crumbled beneath its weight. You would, if found out, be summoned and fined or possibly even imprisoned, and would be deservedly condemned by all right thinking people.

Yet these same righteous people are probably eating as part of their daily food, eggs, veal, pork and so on that are produced by animals kept in these sorts of conditions.

Of course all livestock farming contains an element of cruelty. The animal is not free to roam the country-side, it's confined within the limits of the farm, its sex life is arbitrarily prevented by castration; or by separation from all contact with the other sex. It is being kept for the farmer's profit and for no other purpose, and to that extent is a slave. It seems on the surface to be a contented slave, because it never rebels and also because it can't tell us what it really thinks.

Our treatment of these farm animals has been vastly improved over the term of my farming life. The public, and I must say the farmer's conscience too, has eliminated some of the worst of the practices which used to disgrace us. All slaughter with certain exceptions is preceded by stunning; castration, dehorning and other operations have to be performed with an anaesthetic over a certain age. Market cruelty is being rapidly diminished.

But I think the motivation of this improvement was because the offending practices were spectacular; the squealing of the dying pigs, the bellowing of cattle being winched to the point of slaughter, the blood that bespattered everyone concerned with the more rudimentary farm operations. It's not difficult for the modern conscience to be activated by these things, because they cannot be ignored.

However there are other lines of farming where because the animals are quick and don't display any marked signs of anguish, consciences are pretty inactive. Poultry, veal calves, and pigs are all being increasingly kept under conditions that are giving a few people cause for anxiety, and I am one of them.

I think an animal kept in captivity does deserve the elementary freedom to stretch its limbs, and move around; even in a very confined space. Modern egg production in battery cages no longer fulfils that criterion. When the battery cage was first developed it held one bird, and the idea was that each bird's eggs could be individually recorded. That can no longer apply. Birds are kept several to a cage and so tightly confined that they can no longer either stretch their wings, their legs or their necks without trampling on their companions. Their lives are spent crouched on a sloping wire floor, denied even the scratching and feather dusting that the broilers enjoy on deep litter.

Veal calves are confined in a narrow pen, so narrow that they cannot turn round. Instead of straw, they lie on wooden slats or a wire mesh floor. They take no exercise at all, because to do so would change the colour of their flesh from white to pink. They are not allowed straw because they might eat some and also colour the flesh. In extreme cases their bones crumble and they cannot even walk to the slaughter point. In fairness I should say that so far veal calves are a very small industry here. The calves destined for barley beef, by far the majority, have to be reared so that they can live for at least twelve months.

Pigs are now beginning to be fattened in sweatboxes. This means literally what it says. They are kept so tightly in their sties that they can hardly move, and the temperature is raised by this overcrowding to about 80° Fahrenheit. The principle behind this system seems to be that disease is controlled better at this temperature, than at a lower one.

Those who defend these methods point out that the animals eat well, and either lay well or put on weight, and that this is an indication of the lack of cruelty. Unhappy animals, it's argued, would not thrive. I don't think this is a conclusive argument at all. Confined as they are, they have nothing else to do but eat; and the ingredients in their scientifically blended feeds make their bodies do the rest.

I see no reason at all why these farm animals should not receive the same protection as do the aforementioned; horses, dogs and cats which in the last resort are of no economic value at all.

November 1964   FINANCIAL TIMES

Dung

WHEN I wish to provoke a company of traditional farmers I can usually get a reaction by stating that so far in my farming life, I have never dunged a field; and that any manure that I might make in my cattle sheds was for sale to the first man who offered me any price, or even no price at all for it. Dung to me is a nuisance, like human sewage, and presents much the same sort of problems in its disposal. Mine is of course a special case. My land is cheap, and can carry stock all the winter, and the animals themselves deposit their residues where they will.

But all this does is to save me a deal of trouble, for I don't believe that there is any virtue in farmyard manure that cannot be more cheaply secured through a chemical fertiliser; with the exception of a small amount of humus, which may, or may not, be needed under present farming systems.

After all dung is only the wastage of food consumed by the animal. If that food has been properly utilised, there can be little of real value left in it; although valuations for tenant right still put too high a price on it.

Many farmers seem to be coming to my point of view, but the more they intensify their livestock systems, the more they accentuate their sewage problems. And the further they seem to be from a satisfactory solution. 100 cows in a cowshed in a covered yard lying on straw will produce at least four or five hundred tons of dung in the course of a winter. Enough to cover 25/30 acres fairly thickly. This job can be fairly well mechanised, but it is costly both in time and machinery, and the process is complicated on many farms by the fact that there is no field free of crop or grass to spread it on during the summer, when the yard is empty.

So it has to be hauled out into the field on which it's to be spread and put in a big heap until the clearing of the crop. This has a double disadvantage; the second handling costs almost as much as the first, and the rain and sun bleach out much of the goodness. The only advantage is that the straw content rots down which makes it easier to be absorbed into the soil.

To try to overcome this heavy work some farmers are using a system that uses no straw at all. The cows lie on sawdust in cubicles, which are like cowstalls without the chain, and spend their walking lives on slats. The dung drops through the slats to be held in big tanks, and is eventually either pumped out with an irrigation system or hauled to the fields in a tanker. Others let the residue ooze down to what is called a lagoon at a suitable distance from the buildings. The principle of the lagoon, as far as I understand it, is that the liquid either soaks away into the subsoil, or evaporates in the summer, and the remaining solids are much cheaper to deal with.

These methods are fairly satisfactory, although costly, on a large farm where there is always room to get rid of dung in the end. But intensive beef, pig and poultry units, factory farming systems, present a special problem that is made acute if they have no land attached. A recent Act of Parliament prevents effluent disposal in ditches that might lead to rivers. Local Authorities charge a lot if they are to be attached to the ordinary human drainage systems.

Even farmers with land adjoining these plants are chary of taking the manure as a gift except at times convenient to themselves, and at the expense of the intensive operator. The irony of it is that the bigger the intensive unit, the bigger the traditional farm it needs on which to spread its sewage.

In my case I think tradition has just had a last word. When I bought my farm in Devon two years ago, I had to pay a large sum for dung that the previous occupier had left behind, in various inconvenient places. I passed this farm over to my son this autumn and noticed that the valuation made no mention of dung, a little of which remained. I asked why I hadn't been paid for it, and was told that my son had persuaded the valuer that I didn't think dung was worth anything at all!

November 1964   FINANCIAL TIMES

Smithfield and Pragmatists

WITHIN the last eighteen months I have bought two new and most expensive combine harvesters. These were represented to me as being of the very latest design, and, more particularly as being fully guarded up to the ministry's safety regulations. The combines worked well, but I was enraged, there is no other word for it, when I received a note from the agent the other day to say that the machines were insufficiently guarded. The cost of the new guards would be about £25 plus the cost of fitting.

So to get the annoyance out of my system I decided to visit the manufacturer's stand at Smithfield and complain. After all I always imagined that these shows were a means for improving contacts between manufacturer and their farmer customers. I might well have saved my train fare, in the course of two visits on two separate days I found it impossible to find anyone who was in the least interested in combine harvesters, nor if the truth were told about combine drills either. All they could talk about were their new tractors.

I kept saying that I didn't want to buy a tractor, that

being colour blind I could not tell the difference between their tractor and that of their rivals across the way. That in any case I knew that all British tractors were the best in the world and the cheapest, and also that I suspected that in the words of Kipling like the Colonel's Lady and Judy O'Grady they were sisters under their skin, or paint. In any case I pointed out, performance apart I did not like the new square shape, that reflected all that is ugly in contemporary design. Curves I said suited my farming, curves had lasted horses a good many years, all the best livestock were nicely rounded and so on. He was a polite young man but the look he gave me left me in no illusions that in his eyes I was the only real square at Earls Court.

To restore my self esteem I went to commune with the sheep, always a quiet part of the show. Sheep, like curved radiators, are really out of date at Smithfield. Fat Stock shows should reflect current farming practice and consumer demand. And everyone knows that consumer demand is for lamb and that mutton is a dirty word. With some exceptions the lamb on offer was mutton, and rather fat mutton at that.

Nowhere was this more evident than among the carcases of the crossbred sheep. Most of them, especially the prizewinners, were far too fat and too heavy, although in truth they were much lighter than the monsters common some years ago. The judge though was a North country butcher and for some reason the Northern trade is for much heavier sheep than in the South. There was I suppose some justice in his choice but I would think it reflected a very declining demand.

The light lambs were very good most of them, but I am not going to attempt that market. To make the right weights for Smithfield these have to be born in September. Now Dorset Horns will do this quite well, but other breeds are very difficult. One farmer told me that only twenty-five per cent of the ewes he put to ram in April and May turned out in lamb, and that the cost of keeping the ewes in milk and the lambs thriving was probably higher than the commercial return for out of season lamb would warrant.

Having looked in vain for someone to tell me what the cross-bred sheep demonstration was all about, I went to see what I could learn about bull beef. Bull beef, if you aren't aware of the fact, is what the Jugoslavs sell us, the continentals eat, and that we aren't allowed to produce here except as an experiment. In the carcase section I found a comparison between steer and bull beef that reinforces my belief that castration of barley beef animals is nonsense. The Hereford bull in particular showed that in terms of deadweight gain and lean meat the bull wins hands down. The only obstacle to bull beef production here is the persistence of the Bull Licensing Act.

This continues in force I suppose because the authorities fear that some unscrupulous farmer will pick a promising calf from among his fattening cattle and sell him for breeding. This is nonsense from whichever way you look at it. No sensible dairy farmer is going to buy and use a bull without records and a pedigree behind it. Pure bred Beef bulls are still largely chosen by eye and whether rescued from a beef lot or bought at great expense from a breeder, the resulting progeny would probably be the same. Bull licensing, particularly of beef breeds, is a hidden subsidy to the established breeders and a very definite brake on progress.

If we are to have a continuance of Beef Bull Licensing let it be based on butchers' demands and not on breeders' notions. At Smithfield I did my little bit towards this desirable end by introducing the most famous of all beef bull breeders to a representative collection of wholesale butchers from Smithfield market. It was a distressing commentary on the present state of affairs that each was ignorant of the other's interests and affairs.

To conclude. Have you noticed how fashionable the word Pragmatic has become since the change of government. The Minister uses it to describe his policy and many other writers and speakers have adopted it with enthusiasm. In fact I must be the only one to have avoided it so far, but that was because I was not quite sure what it meant, and being a most responsible commentator I only say what I mean and know that I am meaning.

My interpretation of Mr Peart's use of the word was that he intended to follow the policies of his predecessor until he could think of something else. But I couldn't be sure so I looked it up in the Shorter Oxford Dictionary.

There I find it has a wide variety of meanings including;

busy, active, practical, opinionated, officiously interfering in other people's affairs, dictatorial, dogmatic. And to pragmatise, which is what I imagine a pragmatic Minister does, is to represent what is imaginary or subjective as real. So now you know!

But I trust that any recoupment at the next Price Review will not be just an imaginary sum pragmatised into reality.

A Merry Christmas to you all, and an Oxford Dictionary to Mr Peart with I hope the compliments of the NFU.

December 1964   FARMER AND STOCKBREEDER

The Wind of Change—Cow Style

S CENE: A cobweb-festooned shippon on a broken-down farm in the West of England. It is occupied by two cows. One, a crumpled horned, shelly, potbellied veteran was probably once an Irish Shorthorn. She is the oldest cow in Britain. She was born in 1921, and owes her survival to the fact that her owner has been too ashamed to send her to any sort of market, or even the knacker. The other cow is her remote descendant, showing marked signs of Friesian superimposed on Ayrshire-Guernsey.
The Young Cow speaks first.

YOUNG COW: Why, Gran'ma, your innards are rumbling something awful!

OLD COW: So would yours, dearie, if they had had to deal with what I have put up with all my life.

YC: What's the matter with this lovely barley and the barley straw we've just been given? I heard farmer say it's the latest thing. Scientists say that barley gives high energy, and barley straw has a starch equivalent of 20.

OC: Scientists! If it wasn't for them I wouldn't be as miserable as I am.

YC: Why, what harm could scientists possibly do?

OC: Let me start at the beginning. When I first came into the herd I was fed great helpings of hay and mangolds and swedes and bran and linseed cake. . . .

61

YC: Didn't that make you grunt something awful?

OC: Sure it did. But that just showed it was doing me good. I've heard farmer do that when he came home from market, and he seemed happy enough.

YC: Well, what altered that then?

OC: A fellow called Boutflour. He said all farmers who failed to listen to him were fools, and he said that everyone should feed cows nothing but hay and cake, and that roots and even grass were bad for them. So farmer believed him and we had hay and cake for many years.

YC: Didn't you like that? Just fancy! All your energies could go to milk production, and very few to digestion.

OC: Oh, I survived, because I used to eat my own and other cows' bedding. But many of my sisters died early, having milked themselves to death.

YC: But what changed that?

OC: The war, of course. Cake became short and we were given lots of funny things: new grasses, straw treated with caustic soda, grazing kale in mid-winter in muddy fields. It couldn't be helped, I suppose, but it was nasty while it lasted.

YC: I suppose not. And then?

OC: Grass and silage and nitrogen—grass was so short and rationed by electric fence that we used to gulp it as fast as we could. No wonder we used to blow up.

YC: What happened then?

OC: Farmer used to stick a knife into us to let the wind out, just because he was too mean to put out straw for us to eat, or too ignorant. Or else we used to get the staggers and farmer would come with a bottle and needle and run a lot of dirty water into us. Coo! That used to hurt!

YC: But didn't you get the staggers years ago?

OC: Of course not. I used to have all the grass I could then, and time to eat it in. Nice long stemmy grass of several different kinds.

YC: And what about silage?

OC: Horrible stuff! It's never the same from one layer to the next. Sometimes it's so poor that you can never eat enough, and at others so rich that you go down with acetonaemia. Or it's in self-feed silos that are so tight you can't pull it out without breaking your front teeth. I always dread the winter now because I know farmer is bound to have made some awful silage.

YC: But nitrogen is all right, isn't it? Some of the older girls were telling me that it makes the most delicious young grass, just like the richest cake.

OC: So it does, early in the spring, but the trouble is that he puts more and more on, and we have to graze again and again, and the pasture gets so foul we can hardly eat it. Most insanitary, I call it.

YC: But surely zero-grazing is the answer to that?

OC: Zero grazing, phooey! That damned machine just cuts all the grass and mixes it up. When I graze, I choose the mouthfuls I want, which is a very different thing.

YC: Well, you are an old misery and no mistake! But don't you think it will be nice when we have our nice new cubicles?

OC: What's nice about them, playing musical chairs with a lot of other cows running up and down those slats? Think of the stink from the dung pit. And how do you expect me to back out of those things with my rheumatics?

YC: (*Greedily eyeing the uneaten barley in her neighbour's trough.*) Don't you want to eat your barley?

OC: No, I don't feel like it to-day. Just push me over your straw.

YC: (*Reaches over and quickly scoffs the grain, then stands contentedly for a few minutes, but suddenly feels terribly ill. She begins to blow up and stagger a little. She moans.*) Oh dear, I'm going to die.

OC: You most probably are, my dear. But don't worry. Wasn't it Dr Preston or some other scientist who said that a small number of losses was an acceptable price to pay for the efficiency of barley feeding?

YC: I don't want to be an acceptable price for anything. (*She rolls over quite dead.*)

OC remains sardonically chewing her cud. Then the cowshed radio which has been burbling music during this conversation breaks into voice. The speaker announces that it has been found by scientific test that swedes make an acceptable food for all live stock, and that similar tests are going on with mangolds. OC smiles sardonically, and also dies.

April 1965 FARMER AND STOCKBREEDER

The Fair Deal Fund

I HAVE just had a request for a voluntary contribution to the NFU Fair Deal fund, a matter of 10 per cent of my subscription. Now, while the Price Review has not made me so poor as to make the finding of this sum impossible it has made me extremely cautious of the uses to which I put my money. I naturally don't want to see it wasted. A vast sum of £40,000 or so has been spent by the NFU on advertising in the National Press. Why?

I have not yet heard a logical answer. In fact I have hardly met anyone not connected with farming who even saw the advertisements, let alone remembers what they said. My own experience is, I think, typical. I was told the advertisement was in but I had to look through my paper twice before I came across it. The reason it failed to register was that it was of a class called prestige advertising, such as you see talking about Moral Rearmament and Nationalising Steel. There was nothing to catch the eye, no bargain being offered in striking terms.

However, most farmers I have spoken to seem terribly pleased that their case was in the papers, as no doubt the steel companies were, even though they had paid for it themselves. What they don't realise is that all the impact the Price Review had on the general public was due to the activities of what might be called the extremists in our midst: those who were rude to Mr Peart, or tried to block the roads, or poured a symbolic churn of milk away.

They made the news, and so the general public read about them in the news columns and realised that the farmers were annoyed about something, but they weren't quite sure what.

I am not suggesting that the extremists are right in their manner of drawing attention to their troubles, although it must be admitted that the only way to get anything out of a democratic society is to be consistently unreasonable. But these are tactics of unreason.

It's no good, as Sir Harold Woolley is reported to have done the other day, to threaten industrial action, by which I suppose he means some sort of strike. Although the NFU is a sort of

Union, it has never been classed as an industrial Union, and has had no real experience of striking in support of its claims. If it had, Sir Harold wouldn't be talking such nonsense.

The essential in strike action is that all labour is removed from the employer, and he has either to close down or capitulate. Transferred to our case it would mean a withholding of supplies.

From my contacts with farmers I don't think the Union would get the backing of all, or even a small part of, farmers if it decided to call for a milk strike, the only one that comes to mind. And if a strike were not supported 100 per cent it would be a waste of time. In any case now is not the time to strike. The time to do so is when there is a world food shortage; the reverse is the case at the moment. Apart from a temporary inconvenience, any strike action the Union might call for would be more an annoyance than anything else, but an annoyance sufficient to destroy the remains of the regard in which we are held by the public.

Make no mistake about it, we are most unpopular generally. The public look on us as being completely featherbedded at their expense. I know this is wrong, but the feeling exists, and I find it almost impossible to counter. I was trying to convert a town friend, a professional man, the other day, when down the street swished a Jaguar driven by a prominent local farmer. 'There,' said my friend, 'that's what we do for you! There's X just back from his flat in Spain, to enjoy his swimming pool and the races through the summer. Why should we pay you any subsidies at all?'

It was no good my pointing out that X was one of a tiny minority, the owner of a farming business worth the best part of half a million pounds, who owed his financial success as much to a strategic marriage as to his undoubted skill as a farmer. The harm was done, and is being done everywhere that farmers mingle with taxpayers.

This is the sort of thing the Union is up against, something that no amount of prestige advertising can do anything about. I don't suggest we should all don rags and ride bicycles; or turn our swimming pools, if we have them, into sheep dips.

As a long-term objective I would like to see the burden of the subsidies lifted off the taxpayer and set on the consumer on a business basis. I would like an end to this idea of a special relationship between Agriculture House and the Government. The very term 'special relationship' brings to mind something faintly illicit, like a popsy in a Soho flat.

In wishing this I am only expressing what I believe to be the long-term intention of this and future governments. I think the Union leaders know this too. If they don't, it's time they did. Their task to-day is to plan for a time when markets will be governed either by contrived shortages—quotas—or by the law of the jungle. Time is shorter than they think.

May 1965   FARMER AND STOCKBREEDER

Norman Borlaug

MOST people are becoming aware of the impact of Mexican wheats on the world food situation. In India, Pakistan and other developing countries their adoption means that for the first time in 30 years there should be no need for imports, either purchased or as charity. At the same time the main exporting countries, Canada, Australia and the US, are facing acute problems of surplus.

This dramatic turnround in a situation of stagnant hunger and misery has been due to a large extent to the work of one man, Dr Norman E. Borlaug, of the Rockefeller Foundation, and director of wheat research at the International Wheat and Maize Improvement Centre (CIMMYT) in Mexico.

Borlaug was sent to Mexico by the Foundation some 25 years ago with instructions to assist the country to become independent of imports of wheat, which were an increasing drain on resources as the population grew.

Until he arrived there Borlaug had had little to do with wheat. Born on an 80-acre farm in Northern Iowa, he had worked his way through Minnesota University by running a trap line, coaching football and baseball teams and working as a waiter. He graduated in forestry and, becoming interested in genetics, returned again and worked his way to a degree in that as well.

He is an intensely practical man; indeed, had his father's farm been larger he would have stayed in farming, but he was much influenced by his grandfather—a Norwegian immigrant—who persuaded him to seek education first.

His first experiences in Mexico were discouraging. He was sent to a district of small farms in central Mexico; the occupants were poor, in debt, and, what was far worse, intolerably conservative and suspicious of new ideas. They were fearful of risking any investment in fertilisers and tools for increasing production for which there might not be a market.

He emphasises to-day the importance of showing farmers just how much they stand to gain materially by adopting new techniques. His demonstration fields are heavily fertilised, so that the increased yield is clearly visible to the most sceptical. Once converts begin to be made, governments and bankers will usually provide the resources and the market to make an overall increase possible.

It is essential, he says, that this sort of improvement comes as a package deal. It is no use sowing a new variety unless the farmer has the knowledge to cultivate it, sufficient fertiliser to develop its full potential, and storage and a market for the crop at a fair price. In a world where farmers, scientists, economists and politicians seem to occupy mutually isolationist stances, the achievement of such a policy is a major victory.

He was more fortunate in his appointment to the Yaqui Valley in Northern Sonora. Here the land was being reclaimed from desert by irrigation and the farms were much larger. This was partly because the land was originally almost worthless and also because of a liberal interpretation of Mexican law, which lays down that a man should have no more than 250 acres of irrigated land. This meant capitalist rather than subsistence farming.

Yields in the valley at the time of his arrival were 10 or 12 cwts an acre, the limiting factor being the amount of nitrogenous fertiliser the crop would stand without falling down or lodging so he set to work selecting and breeding short strawed or dwarf wheats.

In Mexico it is possible to have two harvests a year, at

sea level in Sonora in winter and near Mexico City during the summer. This means that a selection can be put into production within three or four years instead of eight or ten under traditional methods.

His selections have been adopted on the main coastal belt with the result that wheat yields on irrigated farming have more than trebled, and Mexico—in spite of a doubled population— has a slight surplus of wheat. Just as important, the high fertility system of wheat growing has led to an overall improvement in rotations and yields of other crops: cotton, soya bean, sorghum and maize.

The main town of the Yaqui Valley, Ciudad Obregon, has grown in 15 years from 15,000 to 125,000 people simply on the prosperity brought about by the farming improvement. The city has just named a street after Borlaug, an unusual tribute to a living American in these parts. Everyone I met gave him full credit for his contribution towards their prosperity.

His work in Sonora is centred on a research station, which is almost entirely financed by the local farmers. Once his success became known he began attracting to it foreign graduates, mainly from the developing countries, for courses of about a year. He insisted that these trainees work as much in the field as in the laboratory, that they get to know farmers, and that they do all manner of practical work.

At the end of their courses many of these young people take away samples to try in their own countries. They find, as Borlaug was sure they would, that some of these Mexican wheats succeed under irrigated conditions in many parts of the tropical belt.

But young graduates, however enthusiastic, can seldom make an impression on their seniors, so Borlaug found that he had to spend weeks each year travelling throughout the developing countries, twisting the arms of the authorities, forcing them to get new types of wheat grown. He has largely succeeded. Mexican wheats and the farming systems to make them work have certainly caught on in wide measure.

Scientists and plant breeders come to the research centre in increasing numbers. He is with them most of the day at harvest time, encouraging his international team to greater efforts. He is far from satisfied with present progress and tells everyone that a two-ton-an-acre crop which is becoming the norm in Sonora is nothing like enough, that the next target should be three (some trial selections have reached this figure). He emphasises the need to keep ahead of rust which develops a new virus to destroy resistant wheat in a very short time.

He is modest about his achievements as a geneticist, claiming that nothing much more than supreme patience and hard work is needed for success. He is tremendously pleased with the success of his wheats in the developing countries, but is quick to tell you that while these, and other crops, can relieve the fear of universal hunger for 20 or 30 years, they will do nothing to prevent the evils of over-population, poverty, unemployment and social disturbance. He is, in essence, he says, buying time for world society to put itself in order.

He will never admit defeat. Theoretically *triticale*, a cross between wheat and rye, should provide the next step in wheat grain development—combining yield and high protein. It has been worked on for 70 years with little success. Now Borlaug is trying again and looks like getting somewhere. He is contemptuous of the new school of scientists which claims that induced mutation of varieties by atomic radiation will save many years of inspection and selection. This may be a touch of the conservatism he himself condemns, but he justifies it by saying that little benefit has come from it so far, and many developing countries which could ill afford such expensive investment would do better with a tithe of it invested in a traditional breeding programme.

In conversation, and in his very scarce publications, he is intensely critical of the conservatism of scientists and of their absorption in basic as opposed to relevant research.

He looks on the present success of his work as only a stage in the development of farming. There is no reason, according to him, why the main cereals, wheat, maize and rice, should not be bred with sufficient protein to provide a full diet, thus avoiding the expense of buying and transporting this material over vast distances.

In his simplistic but practical approach to the solution of farming problems he ranks with the other great innovators of the last 50 years, Sir George Stapledon with Grassland, Dr McMeekan, of New Zealand, with meat and milk, and

Professor Boutflour in Britain with dairying. But the very magnitude of his success makes Borlaug most probably the greatest of all.

June 1966   FINANCIAL TIMES

Advice to Young Hopefuls

I CONTINUALLY get letters from boys or their parents, asking me how they can get into farming. To save me further time and trouble, here is my standard answer:

MY DEAR GEOFFREY,

Thank you for your letter and for your kind enquiry about my health, which is—I can assure you—as good as the times allow. You mention that your father, who was at school with me, has suggested you write to me to see if I can suggest any way you can get into farming.

I remember your father well. He was a very nasty boy, much given to schoolboy blackmail based on his superior age and strength. For two years I was forced to hand over half my pocket money to him.

I used to pray nightly that something awful would happen to him; and in some measure my prayers seem to have been answered. For you state that you want to go into farming because you have no 'O' or 'A' levels, that you are fond of outdoor life, and have no capital nor manual aptitudes, and couldn't bear the thought of joining the labouring classes. In fact you're unemployable.

Obviously, my dear Geoffrey, you couldn't bear the thought of spending the rest of your life as a cowman or pigman. This is something that (provided you were intelligent enough, for 'O' and 'A' levels are not necessarily a standard of common sense) you might in the end be trained for.

The money is not bad, free housing is provided, and you live close to your work. But then of course country sports like shooting, riding and so on will hardly be regular features of your life. Stockmen are not yet so scarce that they have to be bribed to that extent.

So you must keep your sights aimed high—at being a farmer, no less. There are several ways of achieving this. You can inherit £100,000 from a rich aunt, but I fear that you haven't one. You can go into trade or business, work hard for 20 to 30 years and amass a fortune, a part of which you may invest in a country estate on which to farm and lose money for the rest of your days.

I can't help thinking that if you are as stupid as your school record seems to indicate, you may well be a success in business.

I have met many men who have proudly informed me that they have made their fortunes in a business of some sort, and that they now propose to go into farming. But I can only say that the qualities needed for success in business must be very different from those needed in farming; because with a few exceptions they make an unholy mess of the exercise, both financially and technically.

Somehow though, I don't think this approach is for you. It takes a long time, and the result is in no way certain. If you want to go hunting while you can still climb on to a horse without the help of a mounting block, you must go straight into farming.

There are two basic types of farmer. The muddy-booted cowman, or the hunting, shooting, fishing and Jaguar-driving barley baron. The cowman has hard work and money, and the barley baron has sport—and an overdraft.

It's essential, my dear Geoffrey, that you bear these two considerations in mind, for they are fundamental to the success of the operation that I am going to suggest to you.

I take it that you have long ago discarded the old-fashioned notions of romantic love, if indeed you ever cherished them. Because love is essential to the success of the plan. It's perfectly easy, really. Love, as you must know, is a highly controllable emotion. All you have to do is to hold your natural affections—or instincts—in check until you come across the woman who is the possessor of sufficient of the usual feminine attractions, plus a considerable fortune or prospects.

Then turn on the sex appeal.

This of course is an old story, but most cases I have come across have been the result of fortuitous circumstances; yours is to be a planned operation.

You see, I have decided that the only way to get you into farming on your own is for you to marry a farmer's daughter. And a special sort of daughter she has to be, because it's vital that she is the only child, and that her father is elderly, has a weak heart or is drinking himself to death.

You must first of all decide whether to go for mud, cows and money, or sport, barley and an overdraft. I think that you should try the milky way. You see, you need two different sorts of education for these. Cows need hard work and little imagination, barley growing needs big ideas and wide horizons.

You say you know nothing about farming. No matter, you'll be starting with an open mind. It's perhaps a good thing that you have no 'A' or 'O' levels, because otherwise you might have been tempted to go to University. Somehow agricultural graduates seem to have an uncontrollable intellectual arrogance, which would put any girl's father permanently against them.

There are colleges and other places to which you can go without anything much of an education, scholastically speaking. These do produce what might be called standard farming gents, adepts at social life.

You may think that this might get you into the right circles, where you could meet with your prospective prey. Indeed that's true, but the trouble is that while I have never known even a moderate cowkeeper go wrong, it's extremely difficult to spot whether or not the large-scale barley baron is really solvent.

For however much you multiply two tons by the number of acres the farmer says he grows, you will find, on asking the barn man over a pint at the local, that in fact sales are no more than 25 cwt. Further, that mass of mechanisation is on the HP and the fertiliser on extended credit. It takes brains and perspicacity to ferret these things out and frankly, on your record, I don't think you'll do.

With cows it's easier. There are many more cowkeepers and so the field is more open. Dairy farmers' daughters, poor things, are relatively easy to charm. Spending weeks and months in mud and muck helping father makes them ready to clutch at any straw.

So my advice is this: go to a dairying district and get a job—any job—working on a farm and learning to milk. Milking is, as you'll discover, a fairly soul-destroying routine but easily learnt. And because of the chronic shortage of cowmen, the job is one where employers are apt to put up with a good deal of inefficiency.

But your job is only a blind for you to learn the jargon of the trade, and to get you accepted in farming circles—one of which is undoubtedly the Young Farmers Club.

Now this organisation provides the essential arena for marriage strategy. But before you commit yourself you must make absolutely certain that: (a) the prospect's father is more than just solvent, and (b) that he is not likely to live too long. This is most important.

A friend of mine, in just the same case as you are to-day, married the daughter of an ailing dairy farmer 35 years ago. Since then he has milked 14 times a week; his father-in-law is still hale and hearty and well in command of the situation; his wife has run off with the undertaker. This just shows that even if you attempt this operation the hard way, the rewards are by no means certain.

Another thing to remember is that women these days have more say in the disposal of their money. It would be a pity if you went to all this trouble to marry the girl and the farm, and she still kept a tight hold on the money, so defeating your object of selling the cows and becoming a barley baron.

Well, my dear boy, that's the best I can do for you. If only you were a Welsh-speaking graduate from Bangor, what avenues of agricultural bureaucratic advancement would lie open to you. But you aren't, so you'd better go into your father's business—or aren't you even bright enough for a betting shop?

December 1966   FARMER AND STOCKBREEDER

Geoffrey Sykes

'**Y**OU see, John, Hagedorn says that if you inbreed chickens to the nth degree, you will have to cull 99 out of every hundred of the progeny, but the 100th will give you a strain of birds that will survive the ills of inbreeding, to the limit of their economic life and have all the qualities necessary for economical egg production.'

The circumstances of this pronouncement have remained fixed in my memory although it happened 20 years ago. Geoffrey Sykes and I had played truant from a solemn grass seed meeting at Aberystwyth to climb Snowdon. Now in general I am no mean talker myself, but my constitution is such that I cannot talk and climb mountains at the same time, so I was subjected to the stream of Geoffrey's enthusiasm without the chance of talking him down. I was too hot and bothered at the time to take a very intelligent interest in what he was saying, but the message got through, and it was stored somewhere in my subconscious whence it regurgitates from time to time for there is something subliminal about his propagandising.

For nearly 30 years now he has been pumping out ideas from his farm base at Berwick St James, near Salisbury, and he has had more influence over the poultry industry than any other man. His gifts are not those of the researcher or the breeder, or even of the commercial man, although he has been moderately successful at all three. He is much more one to seize on the ideas of others, to adopt them as the present ideal and to push them with all his very great powers of advocacy. And then, when he finds something he considers better, he loses no time in discarding the old for the new, often with bewildering suddenness.

As he practises what he preaches, he loses no time in changing his methods to suit the new ideas, and this in farming is no certain road to financial success; change costs money. The poultry tycoons are those who have stuck to their established lines long enough to exploit them fully, but most of them will admit to the debt they owe to Geoffrey Sykes' ideas and imagination.

The mainspring of his inspiration has been the United States which he first visited on a Government mission in the 1940's and has revisited constantly since. There is something appealing to him in the bigness of American business thought, in the scale of its operations, in the resolute scrapping of anything remotely out of date or out of fashion.

He was among the first to recognise the benefits of controlled hybridisation, which is the basis of all chicken breeding to-day. It is, thanks again to the scale of their operations, largely an American monopoly to-day since few British companies have the resources to compete in this field, and most of them are associated with one or other of the American giants. He has been a constant critic of the established breeders of cattle, sheep and pigs, but so far these animals have not been as easy meat for the geneticist to control as poultry.

He was the pioneer of the henyard, which subsequently became the deep litter house, where hens live and scratch in their own excreta and, if the ventilation is properly controlled, do extremely well there for litter under ideal conditions seems to sterilise itself. This system is out of favour at the moment, because it lacks the easy control of individual birds that is part of the battery system. But Sykes has persisted with it, and now claims that in his deep litter, environmentally-controlled houses, he has a hen housed average egg production exceeding that of the best battery stock, and at a much lower capital cost.

He has no broilers now, although he was the main pioneer of their introduction and development in Britain. This followed a Nuffield Scholarship to the States in the early 1950's. For the next few years he pushed broilers by every means he could think of. Many people came to listen, to scoff, to think again, and to imitate, and some of his imitators have become very rich men indeed, but not Geoffrey. It's not that he is indifferent to commercial success; most of his schemes are founded with that expectation, indeed he was for several years a powerful advocate of what the Americans call Agri-business. That is a complete integration of farming processses from the basic seed or semen, through to the consuming public. The complete antithesis of the traditional farmer's craft. So far even in the States it's only confined to the broiler industry.

Of late years though he has been abandoning the technical

side of poultry farming, probably because the industry is consolidating after the immense changes of the last 20 years, and applying himself more to the commercial exploitation of the business, but not in the narrow confines of this island. He had plans that nearly came to fruition for a tax-privileged broiler industry in Eire, which was to supply the rest of Europe. That having been pipped, he is deeply involved with some American associates in an international poultry franchise covering almost all the undeveloped—poultrywise—countries of the world.

While I was gathering material for this article, I had the greatest difficulty in extracting from him the historical facts of his career; he kept turning the conversation to the present and particularly to the future. His imagination is just as lively as it was when I first knew him more than 30 years ago; long may it remain that way, such minds are rare and should be cherished as one of farming's precious assets.

January 1967   FINANCIAL TIMES

The Handicap of a Formal Education

A GOOD deal of dust and heat is being raised by the reported threat of the University Grants Committee to abolish the agricultural departments of certain of our universities. The first victim is said to be Leeds, and Glasgow and Cambridge are also alleged to be in danger. The grounds for this discrimination are not known. Perhaps these faculties are not so adept at keeping in the public eye as are some of the others.

In academic matters, as well as everything else in modern life, humility gets you nowhere.

So it's a good time to consider the whole picture of agricultural education. By that I mean education taught by academics rather than by practical farmers. It's possible that I am not the man to do it. I have no experience of formal agricultural education, and my only excursion into university life was to spend two terms studying textiles at Leeds.

I could have gone to Cambridge to read agriculture, for in

those days the only entrance qualification was your father's ability to pay the fee. This I insisted I should retain myself, to help me start farming on my own.

I have never regretted this decision because I am increasingly convinced that the only way to learn farming is at the grass roots, on the farm, with your own money. The reason for this is simple. Those who teach farming, be it in farm institutes, colleges or universities can never be practical men.

This is no fault of theirs, of course. They may be practical in that they know how to feed a beast or grow a crop. But they seem to be unable to marry the practical work with the criterion of whether it pays or not. And profit, call it by any word you like, is the only thing that really counts.

If you doubt my word, look around at your successful neighbours. How many of them had any formal agricultural education at all, especially those who started on a shoestring? I bet you hardly find one.

I grant you there is the odd exception to the rule, but he in most cases started with a certain amount of capital and his formal education was probably nicely diluted with common sense.

Ah, you will say, times are different now, units are getting bigger, it is the day of the scientific farmer, those who rely on simple experience and common sense will be relegated—if they get in to the industry at all—to the menial tasks at the bottom of the wages structure, beneath the dignity of the Training Board.

You know, the same thing was being said, except of course about structure and the training boards, more than 40 years ago, and will probably be repeated 40 years on as more and more trained, graduated and other qualified individuals look for places in farming.

By this time I expect that most of you are with me to the extent of agreeing that the higher a man's agricultural academic education, the more useless he is to practical farmers.

Usefulness in this sense goes by stages: a graduate is absolutely useless, a diploma holder less so, and for a boy from a good farm institute there is some little hope.

The trouble is, the institutions we rely on for practical advice are being increasingly staffed by graduates who are by their very training academics. The higher their qualifications the higher the positions they hold in the hierarchy. If the husbandry farms were run by commercial farmers for profit, wouldn't they carry more conviction than under their present controllers?

I rather doubt if we want specialist agricultural university departments at all. We do need specialists and we do need researchers, but they needn't have had an agricultural training. A botanist or biologist or an economist can apply these skills to anything within their field at any time within their working lives. They need know nothing of practical farming, for the practical people can use the findings of these specialists in the light of their own practical experience.

From the students' point of view there would be advantages if there were no agricultural faculties. Then graduates in the pure sciences would have the choice of many fields in which to work without the limitation that specialising in agriculture brings to their careers. Farm processes are always changing, and they could enter the agricultural field at any time on equal terms with those in it.

Colleges and institutions are more practical in their approach, but they suffer the fatal drawback that they are largely staffed by people who have never farmed at a profit. So, of course, is the NAAS.

Their advantage is that they do provide a place where farmers' sons and daughters can go and mix with other farmers' sons and daughters and so broaden their ideas, but these young people would probably benefit even more from some completely non-farming surroundings for a while.

If we do need formal training in the future I would sooner see it in the shape of the severely practical. I believe—and I have said this often before—that far from enlarging into big units, farming is going to become largely composed of one-man or family concerns, as it is in the States and Australia.

Formal training should be directed towards helping farmers to adapt to these circumstances. So far there is no sign that my thesis has been accepted, officially at least, but it's happening all the same.

February 1967   FARMER AND STOCKBREEDER

Sometimes JOC's blunt views gained a vigorous response from readers, as shown by these ripostes to the preceding article.

Deplorable, Mr Cherrington

As an undergraduate in agriculture I utterly deplore Mr Cherrington's article.

I admire him as a practical farmer, but I never thought a man of his undoubted intelligence would make such a sweeping condemnation. Admittedly an academic education can be misdirected when it takes no account of the practical situation, but I would venture to suggest that these cases are rare and reflect inadequacies in the individual rather than in the system of education.

Mr Cherrington suggests that university places would be better used training specialists. This would only weaken his argument by divorcing the practical from the academic even more than he suggests it is at the moment. There must be a place for trained agriculturists even if it is only to integrate these specialists and to act as a liaison between them and the practical farmer.

Is Mr Cherrington suggesting that the only way to learn farming is the hard way, by experience and trial and error? Surely the industry today cannot tolerate such an expensive form of education? The training of the mind that an academic education imparts is surely cheaper and safer in the long run.

I. J. M. FROOD
Reading, Berks.

I did not believe that anyone, John Cherrington included, could talk such nonsense! I am glad to see that editorial opinion does not necessarily concur with the writer's views.

It is ridiculous to correlate an academic training with an absence of business acumen.

John Cherrington's emphasis of practical farming which suggests 'how' rather than 'why', sounds a useless single qualification for keeping pace with changes and progress.

W. B. LIGHTWING
Collingham, Wetherby, Yorks.

John Cherrington's questions about the merits of higher education for intending farmers is intended to be provocative. I fear that it is possible by over-simplification to create the wrong impression of the value of such an education.

University and college education is not advisable for everybody, or possible for everybody. I think it would be wrong, however, to infer that it was likely to be a disadvantage; on the contrary, many of us owe a great deal to the education we have had, not only in increasing our store of knowledge but, as is the purpose of education generally, in developing our minds and using them better.

Mr Cherrington is perfectly entitled to point out that many people have been able to succeed without the benefits of higher education, but it would be wrong and doing a disservice to many parents and sons if he failed to recognise that there were very substantial advantages to be got from it.

W. R. TREHANE
Chairman, MMB
Thames Ditton,
Surrey

How can a presumably intelligent, successful, far-sighted businessman be so dogmatic and narrow-minded?

I suggest that many of the farmers who started on a shoe string and who are now successful would be the first to admit that they would never have made the same progress without the inflated profits of the post-war period. Had they had the knowledge and technical know-how of to-day's agricultural graduates they may have made even better progress.

John Cherrington says that a graduate is absolutely useless to practical agriculture [but I would say that] the examples of successful farmer-graduates are too numerous to mention.

IAN C. PEARSON
University of Nottingham,
School of Agriculture,
Sutton-Bonington

I enclose two letters which I imagine might well be written if Mr Cherrington's opinions of Formal Education are to be taken seriously.

1. 'To The Chief Education Officer, County Council: With reference to my grant for a three-year course in agriculture at

Redbrick University, I am wondering whether I might cancel my place and have the full sum as I would rather go farming. You will appreciate that this will be a much better training.

'My father is an insurance clerk. Do you think this will spoil my chances in agriculture?'

2. 'The Editor, Woman's Very Own: Newly married and hardly able to boil an egg, I am so glad that I have never been taught how to cook. My husband comes home tired and hungry and when I've nothing for him to eat I know he's thinking what a wonderful cook I'll be in the end—learning the hard way. We're happy.'

S. HOLMES (MRS)
Vine Farm,
Worplesdon, Surrey

March 1967   FARMER AND STOCKBREEDER

Universities—My Views Are Unchanged

OF the twenty-three letters that were published in *Farmer and Stockbreeder* as a result of my article on agricultural education, 17 attacked me with various degrees of intolerance, three could be described as more or less neutral (i.e., I could not understand their logic), and three supported me. Fair enough; but this majority opinion has done nothing to alter my views.

You see, of the 17 that attacked me, at least 14 came from people with a vested interest in the continuance of the present system, writing mostly from colleges, universities and other seats of learning. Very few indeed came from full-time practical farmers. This suggests to me that even if farmers want the present educational system to go on, they are not in any hurry to rush into print to save it.

I should say here, though, that I was told by a member of the body which is responsible for the suggested closure of the faculties that I named that the publicity, or otherwise, surrounding certain personalities in the educational world has nothing to do with the closure decisions. The decision was based on an estimate of the numbers of graduates required and the number of faculties necessary to produce them. I am glad to publish this correction.

Now, if you read my article thoroughly you would have seen that I did not condemn all university education. What I did say, and I stick to it, was that trying to teach practical farming as a university course is nonsense. In fact it is the negation of what I take to be the essential of a university course, which should be to broaden the avenues of learning.

Practical farming is basically a simple operation, consisting of maximising the gap between costs and returns. The tools of the trade are practical skills and a sort of spiv mentality for buying and selling. You don't get this sort of training at any university that I know of, nor much of it at the other seats of learning.

But I'm all for University education for those who can afford the time and the money to go there. Two of the best farmers I know are graduates, but one took history and the other natural sciences. I repeat they had the capital and could afford the time, and their minds are well broadened by their experience. I doubt if they would have been improved at all by reading agriculture. Let's leave it at that.

I must touch on a kindred subject; the Agricultural Training Board. This, I gather, is going to cost us money; 2½ per cent on the wages bill is the suggested figure. The money collected is, after deductions for administration, to be used to pay farmers who train young people on their farms. It's a sort of compulsory replacement for the now moribund apprenticeship scheme.

Now I am quite happy to train young people at my own expense, and in my own methods, and have been doing this all my life, as and when I have needed replacement. Nor do I think there is any shortage of skilled men. If 20,000 are leaving farming every year, it's simply because farmers have no work for them at the sort of wages they can get elsewhere.

Training more men will make no difference, if the pay and prospects are not comparable with what they get in industry. So why should we be saddled with this incubus?

I have had no satisfactory answer to this. It seems that the NFU and the Trade Unions have cooked it up between them without, as far as I can gather, consultation with the rank and file of farmers. This would not matter, were it not for the levy, which I gather is going to be a statutory obligation. About as bad a case of taxation without representation as I know.

If I refuse to pay I can, I suppose, in the end be jailed, but I think I am too old to be a martyr. So I shall probably deduct the cost of the levy from my increased NFU subscription, which will serve the so and so's right for getting their priorities wrong.

April 1967   FARMER AND STOCKBREEDER

In November 1967 JOC started writing a column for the New Zealand Farmer. *His brief was to report on trends and developments in British farming and on policies of interest to New Zealand farmers, especially regarding the European Community.*

Militant Farmers

ONE Saturday last December about a hundred Devon farmers drove into the small market town of Newton Abbot. Slowly they perambulated the streets and successfully managed to disrupt traffic for an hour before they withdrew in response to pleas from the police to do so.

There is nothing illegal about driving a tractor into town, but to do it in organised numbers is classed as a demonstration, and in this democracy, demonstrations have to be arranged beforehand with the police.

Since then the number of these affairs has multiplied, culminating at the time of writing with a mob of Huntingdonshire farmers besieging the Prime Minister during a visit to a research station in that county.

The PM's response to this was to thank them for coming, which just about sums up the official reaction. But there is no doubt that these activities have secured the farmers a far better coverage in the National Press than all the efforts of the National Farmers Union's highly-costly publicity department.

The mainspring of the movement has been a Devon farmer, Wallace Day, who for years has criticised the NFU's acceptance of the price review and all its works, on the very real grounds that farmers were being progressively under-recouped for their labour and investment.

Farm prices here have risen very little over the past 10 years, while costs are estimated to have gone up more than 60 per cent.

During this time the price of food to the housewife has risen by between 30 and 40 per cent.

The effect of the squeeze on income has particularly hit farmers in the more marginal areas, but my impression is that these pressures are affecting almost all farmers and, very often, those most likely to survive are the small, family-type farms.

Those employing one or two men are getting into real trouble, especially where the land has been bought at the present level of high prices or where capital expenditure has been incurred with borrowed money. Overdrafts now cost at least 10 per cent and this takes a bit of finding.

Mr Day was a member of the council of the National Farmers' Union and resigned in exasperation a few weeks ago to lead the Farmers Action Group which is responsible for the militancy, but he has since been triumphantly re-elected to it.

The union's president Sir Gwilym Williams has done his best to steal Mr Day's thunder by matching the latter's demands for satisfaction at the February Price Review.

Meanwhile, the more Establishment-minded farmers are deploring the whole thing as being in markedly bad taste. The demonstrations are to continue on a countrywide basis until the Price Review.

The most likely casualty will be the removal of Sir Gwilym Williams from the scene. He has been very much criticised over the years for his apparent acquiescence to Government and authority generally.

Criticism is a large part of all British political life and the NFU is no exception. Office holders have to learn to live with it, but there comes a time when the weight of criticism overcomes the incumbents.

Whether the new man, probably Mr Henry Plumb the deputy president, will do any better is problematical. If the review is a good one, or can be shown to be a good one he may be off to a good start but, if it's not, there may be a pretty rough time for the NFU all round, with action groups impotently harassing Ministers and stopping traffic all over the country.

The impotence is simply because the Government holds all the aces and determines the level of the deficiency payments. Farmers can take no strike action or other sanction because they are disunited and there is plenty of temperate food in the world just trying to get into these islands.

This state of affairs is making farmers look a lot more favourably towards the Common Market. There is no doubt the attraction is the high level of prices operating there, coupled with the levies on imports that will bid fair to keep a lot of the competition at bay.

The theory is that the EEC system will lead to the encouragement of more home production to avoid the levies on imports from the Commonwealth or high-priced imports from the Common Market countries and that, within these prices, efficient British farmers (and they are economically efficient by European standards) would have no trouble in doing pretty well.

This notion is being carefully nurtured by both political parties and by the pro-Market lobbies, with the Conservatives being the most articulate. They have already proposed a levy system on the Continental model and their disregard of Commonwealth ties—obligations no longer seem to exist—is absolute. In this case the line is that the Commonwealth has other outlets, meaning the Far East and, in any case, why did the New Zealanders buy those Boeing jets?

At the same time, Government propaganda is pushing the line that the Six will have to reorganise their farming in any case and that the prices there will not be so high in a few years time.

This is dangerous wishful thinking. I am at present engaged in a long-term study of EEC farming, visiting all the countries, and of one thing I am becoming certain: there will be no reduction in EEC prices and that the barriers against food imports are likely to get higher, rather than lower.

At the same time, the stored surpluses are beginning to shrink; that expected for butter has failed to meet its target by some 70,000 tons, and those for wheat and sugar are beginning to come under control.

Figures used by the EEC Commission, particularly for grain stocks, are being attacked as inaccurate. In fact, the pressures for reform will become less as the surpluses are not so apparent. Dr Mansholt and his plan have been shelved indefinitely.

I have been setting out a broad picture of our farming scene so that the happenings of the next months which I will be writing about can be put in some sort of perspective.

It's true that it's mainly political, but then politics really dictate our survival. Most of us in farming know how to cope with the weather, the land and the various diseases and pests that afflict us. If it weren't for the politicians we would be millionaires.

For my part, I farm about 1,000 acres in Hampshire about 60 miles west of London; 700 acres are cropable on which I grow 400 acres of barley, 150 acres of wheat and 50 to 100 acres of ryegrass seed.

I have 1,100 breeding ewes, Greyfaced, bred out of a Swaledale ewe by a Bluefaced Leicester ram and purchased as ewe lambs in the Pennines in the North of England.

There are a few cattle to eat the surplus grass and hay and a herd of pigs is being built up to 120 sows.

The main income is from the sale of grain, grass seed and prime lambs but, eventually, I hope to convert a good proportion of my grain into pigmeat and expect to get the major part of my gross income from this source.

My labour force consists of my son, who is building up the pig business, one man erecting buildings for the pigs and four men to work the arable and sheep. This is rather a high labour figure, but I use them to make up a team with two other sons who farm nearby so that we can get the economies of scale in working a total of 1,100 acres of arable among us.

You should remember that our seasons are very short and also that I am now of pension age, better fitted to drive a typewriter than a tractor.

November 1967   NEW ZEALAND FARMER

Long Ago When I Was Young

DID I ever tell you how I learnt to milk? It was in New Zealand, and I had emigrated there [in 1929] thinking in my innocence that pastures 12,000 miles away from home would be greener and very much cheaper. I was sadly disillusioned as to the cheapness of the land, but the pastures were certainly green, and so was I.

My knowledge of farming at that time was scant. I had spent six months on a farm in the South Midlands where the main activity had been fattening cattle, but all that taught me was that fattening cattle would never be profitable enough for me. I had played tennis, and begun an acquaintance with the trout which has given me endless pleasure and interrupted my flow of life considerably ever since. But I hadn't learnt how to do the ordinary menial tasks on a farm, for graziers lived like gentlemen in those days.

Eventually I got to New Zealand, and went to meet a man who wanted a boy to work on his farm. I met him at the local show, and he was a smartly dressed soldier type. I wouldn't say we took to each other like a house on fire, but he obviously wanted help, and I wanted a job, and that was that; it was agreed that I should go there a few days later.

I was driven to the farm, many miles up an earth road between gorges of bush and thorn, and in the end we got to the house: a bungalow, very isolated, surrounded by some pine trees and red roofed buildings. The farmer came out and met us. I was determined to make a good impression and I had always been told that the way to success in New Zealand was never to refuse to do a job, never to say 'I can't', always to give it a go. So when he said, 'Can you milk?' I said, 'Oh yes, I can milk all right.'

I knew the theory. You sat down under a cow, you squeezed its teats, and the milk came forth. 'Well,' he said, 'the black cow's down in the bail, here's the bucket, and tea's ready when you've finished.'

I was pretty hungry, so I took the bucket and went to the bail. The bail was just a shed beside the wool shed, and in it was an old Angus cow tied by the neck and with a leg rope on, and there was a stool. I sat down beneath her, applied myself to her teats.

To say that she was a hard milker would be no exaggeration, but to say that I knew nothing about it would be no exaggeration either. I squeezed and I pulled, and I squeezed again and eventually managed to get a thin wavering stream directed into the bucket. Fortunately she couldn't kick it over because her leg was tied back, but her bag remained as tight as ever. Meanwhile the milk at the bottom of the bucket hardly rose at all.

At last I got about half an inch; my arms were aching and I had no more strength in my fingers at all.

There was a little stream, or creek as they call it in New Zealand, running outside the building, and I went down the bank, tipped the bucket into the water, and put about 3 in. of the creek water along with the milk. It looked all right. When I took it up to the house, because by this time I was famished as well as paralysed in the arms, the boss said: 'Huh, you've done well, boy; I never thought she gave as much as that in the evenings.'

We all had tea, and the next morning I milked rather better, and had to add a little less water, and eventually, after a week or so, I managed to milk her right through without the addition of any H_2O.

Nobody spotted the varying consistency of the milk except possibly the child of the household, who was about nine months old and who went through a whining stage for several days. But, anyway, the baby couldn't talk, and neither of the parents drank milk, except in tea, so they didn't know.

During all this time I continued shaving daily, although dressed in rags, maintaining (as I had been advised to at home) the standing of an Englishman among the colonials. The boss never shaved at all unless he went to town, and as things were terribly bad financially, he never went to town and became hairier and hairier. At last he drew me aside one morning and said: 'John, if you want to keep the job, you will stop shaving. The wife has been making comparisons'. So I stopped shaving, and the wife just had no choice.

Life in New Zealand was certainly hard in those days. The

people were terribly kind, but the prices were absolutely rock bottom; lambs under 6d a pound, wool was down to about 8d and milk around 4d per gallon.

Land prices still remained high, even in the depths of the depression, while prices of everything sold dropped and dropped. But farmers kept going, because there was no alternative employment except in towns and these were just as depressed as the farms.

Farmers survived by spending no money, and never doing anything which could be left undone without affecting the main issue. It was wonderful training for farming in England during the 30's when I came home and I was very grateful for it, but it was pretty miserable from time to time while I was there.

Jobs were so hard to get that you just clung to one until another came along, and put up with all sorts of difficulties and discomforts. I always preferred sheep work. It wasn't hard, and although the hours were long—particularly mustering and shearing—you were pretty much your own boss. But once in a moment of enthusiasm, I think to get money for motor bike repairs, I took a job harvesting.

Now the farmer I went to had a very good farm, but it had been badly flooded the previous year and he had been absolutely skinned out. He borrowed enough money to plant another crop, but that was all. He offered me fair pay, but said: 'I can't pay you until harvest is over and I have sold a bit of corn.'

It was a binder harvest in those days, he drove the binder and an old Irishman and I did all the stooking. There were 250 acres of corn, wheat and oats. The wheat yielded 60 bushels (or 15 sacks) and the oats 120 bushels. I have never seen such oats, and the Irishman and I stooked them all ourselves, and then when we had stooked them we turned round and with teams of horses set to work to carry them into rick.

Very often in those days the thrashing machine would thrash straight from the field, but because of the danger of wet weather we ricked as much as we could, never thatching the ricks of course. We built about two dozen ricks and big ones they were too; and we engaged another helper, a half caste Maori who was the champion sheaf tosser of the district.

We would load four wagons with sheaves, and bring them

back to the rick. There were no elevators. The Irishman and the Maori threw the sheaves up to the top of the rick, I caught them on my prong (I was what they called crow) and passed them to the boss who built the rick.

There was a high wind blowing most of the time, the Maori threw the sheaves with terrific force and every now and then one completely missed me, or I missed it, or else it carried my prong down towards the boss's legs.

He was a miserable man at the best of times, and could do nothing but grumble. If he had to move a sheaf after I had placed it in front of him, it was cause for another grumble about the uselessness of the English, and the excellence of everybody else. At last I got flustered, and missing the sheaf, managed to stick one of the prongs in his leg. I withdrew it carefully, and he never said a word; he never said a word any more. I think he thought I meant it.

He had to keep me another three weeks until his money came, and he could pay me. After that I left New Zealand for the Argentine, where I found it was no easier to keep a job, I wonder why?

December 1967   FARMER AND STOCKBREEDER

Noticed Girls' Legs Lately?

IT'S not often that one gets a preview of the contents of the Price Review award, but I came across the following when haunting a Whitehall bar. It concerns meat production, and is based on work carried out in France by a society of Cuissophiles (in English, the study of girls' legs). It appears that since the advent of the miniskirt, the thighs and legs of girls exposed to the elements have developed an extra layer of fat and flesh to protect their circulatory systems.

I must say that I had noticed something of the sort myself, but never pursued my researches to the point of using a tape measure on comparative anatomies. But the French have. And have decided that the effect of miniskirts has been to induce an increase of 5 per cent in fat, and no less than 7 per cent in flesh on the exposed portions.

The results of this work are now being applied to cattle and sheep at centres in France and the USA. Selected animals are having portions of their skins shaved or shorn and then are being exposed to the elements, in order to see if the same build up of fat and flesh takes place. The portions to be shaved cover those parts where the most valuable cuts are situated, the loin and rump. The system cannot be applied to pigs, as they are more or less hairless as it is. But it's pointed out that they are the quickest fleshing of all animals, and remarkably similar to humans in their physiological and psychological behaviour.

That's all I can disclose for the moment, except that I gather the Meat and Livestock Commission is very excited about it and making it a No. 1 priority for its funds. The Minister is said to regard it as providing a real breakthrough in British beef production, and likely to remove the need of any other financial inducement in tomorrow's Review.

• • •

March 1968   FARMER AND STOCKBREEDER

JOC was a keen traveller and he was never afraid to put his findings into print. This article on New Zealand got a sharp response from both the farming establishment and the government.

Lean Period Ahead for the Farmers

AN outstanding trait of the New Zealand character is a stubborn refusal to face the facts of modern economic life: I have no doubt about this. Individually, New Zealanders are hard working and efficient. Their climate is favourable to the growing of grass; they have a pathological aversion to subsidy; they are the most efficient producers of milk, meat and wool in the world. Therefore, the national reasoning goes, they should be able to survive.

This concept of virtue being economically rewarded permeates all sections of society. If anything goes wrong, if butter proves unsaleable or the Americans introduce quotas on meat—and in consequence there are credit squeezes, import restrictions and threats of rising unemployment—it is 'most unfair.' Quotas should go. The EEC and Britain should give up their subsidy and other immoral practices as soon as possible, so that New Zealand could be geared once again to the job for which, it seems, the Lord has created these isolated islands.

Not that the underlying crisis is very evident to the casual visitor. During the holiday season, which seems to run from December through to February, the lakes, sea and mountains, are crowded to an extent that makes accommodation difficult to find. The cars on the still empty roads are dragging an impressive proportion of power boats and caravans. Everyone is healthy, sunburnt and huge.

But this prosperity is only skin deep. Farming is still responsible for 88 per cent of the country's foreign earnings and this proportion is unlikely to be much reduced in the foreseeable future unless a viable and competitive industry could be developed or a scarce mineral comes to light. Without such a miracle, New Zealand could remain a pastoral country for ever more, a Falkland Islands on the grand scale.

The country depends for its existence on the profits to be earned from a world trade in food which is becoming increasingly dominated by the surpluses of countries whose economies are primarily industrial and who find it worth their while to subsidise their farmers directly or protect them by tariff walls.

The difficulties of the dairy market are well known. Subsidised competition from almost everywhere else has reduced the price paid to New Zealand farmers for butter fat by 25 per cent over the last two years. To counter this they have been increasing their stocking rates so that production is rising at a rate of 4 per cent annually. Not enough to counter the fall in return but enough to make their economic survival possible for a few more years or until times improve.

There have been amalgamations, some of the smaller units have been absorbed by their neighbours, but in the main cow density has gone up from one cow to one and a half acres 10 years ago to nearly two cows an acre on the best farms to-day. The farm unit is still largely a one-man enterprise; but instead of 60 cows, the farmer and his wife are probably looking after and milking double that number.

At present the New Zealand Dairy Board, a farmers' organisation which markets the dairy products of the whole country, is determined to keep on producing at an increasing annual rate in the hope that other suppliers of the international markets will get tired of the game and leave virtue (the New Zealand virtue of low cost at any price) to be suitably rewarded. This may take a very long time, but such items as a vestigial fall in Swedish and American cow numbers are taken as a good sign for a brighter future—with the same enthusiasm as a drowning man clutches a straw.

There is no subsidy on dairy exports at the moment. Prices are being maintained at the new low levels through the operation of a reserve fund, built up when times were good. This is now in deficit, and the money to finance it is borrowed from the Government at 1 per cent interest. Even so, another price reduction to farmers will probably be needed to prevent the deficit from getting out of hand.

There are of course other importing markets than Britain, but these have been thoroughly exploited by dumping from the richer countries and the EEC. The present New Zealand solution, put forward with pathetic earnestness by everyone from Mr Holyoak downwards, that surpluses should be given to the hungry people is a non starter. No one seems to have the money to pay for the operation.

Meat accounts for nearly 40 per cent of the country's earnings; and after a short period of comparative stability due to foot-and-mouth and the absence of Argentine supplies, the British market looks like weakening again. Lamb, the main export to Britain, is increasing at a rate of 1m. head a year, and in spite of expensive efforts to sell elsewhere, particularly in North America, these extra supplies seem almost certain to come to Smithfield once again.

I have never thought New Zealand meat was well sold in

Britain. For instance, the average New Zealand lamb to-day brings the farmer about 50s. For the same weight of animal the English farmer would get more than double before the subsidy payment. If £1 is allowed for transport and storage there would appear to be a margin of 30s a lamb which looks to be the measure of the inefficiency of the system, and one that I would have thought farmers in New Zealand would do their best to eliminate; particularly when it is realised that freezing does not destroy lamb quality, as it does that of beef.

Apart from lamb, 91 per cent of which comes to Britain, the other main exports are beef to the US, and mutton to Japan. The beef is largely manufacturing grade, and the mutton unsaleable elsewhere. Australia is a substantial competitor in these markets but does share a voluntary beef quota with New Zealand for the US. This quota will not be sufficient to absorb the increasing production of both countries, and in the absence of other markets the combined surplus expected of 150,000 tons is almost bound to be sent to Britain. There just is nowhere else. Exports of mutton have been affected by the Australian drought, which caused heavy selling by that country to Japan, and there are at present large stocks in New Zealand stores.

Wool, the other part of the stock farmers' income, is making a rather better showing after the fall two years ago. But the higher prices are partly due to devaluation, and mainly for the finer grades. Coarse wools at present account for 70 per cent of the output and this proportion would be hard to change for husbandry reasons.

On the whole the meat and wool farmers have had a harder squeeze than the dairymen. The 40 per cent drop in wool prices two years ago caused a complete crumbling of confidence. Men were dismissed and routine fertilising and maintenance was much reduced. Phosphate plants reduced output and aerial topdressing firms lost money. Production is still increasing because of past measures now coming into effect, and the farmers' habitual reaction to hard times of increasing output to outdistance rising costs. Nevertheless 25 per cent of farmers, mainly recent entrants and small scale operators, are believed to be going downhill financially.

They do not get much sympathy from their more established fellows or the urban population. Federated Farmers, the equivalent of the NFU, is considered by the few independently-minded dissidents I have come across as a hotbed of large farmers devoted above all to free enterprise, opposed to any outside advice.

But something surely must be done. New markets have been sought with some success, but at a very heavy cost. And these are extremely vulnerable to dumping or other obstacles put up by richer countries. Increased production is bringing serious problems in its train. Because of overstocking, wool quality is falling, particularly in Southland. The individual weight of the lamb kill is showing a falling tendency. Cattle mortality is rising, partly because of the difficulties of providing winter feed.

These are all symptoms of shortage of cash to enable farmers to do the job properly. Production could well begin to fall, unless the New Zealand Government and farm organisations swallow their pride, and start subsidising farming, so following the example of the Danes, who were fanatically opposed to farm subsidies until they were forced to adopt them to maintain their markets, and export earnings. It will be a momentous affront to the New Zealand philosophy, but without some form of farm subsidy, New Zealand looks like losing ground in the present state of the world's food game.

February 1969   FINANCIAL TIMES

New Zealand Farming—
No 'Doctrine of Despair'

Wellington—New Zealand farming, unlike that of many other countries, can stand on its own feet.

This claim was made in a statement by the New Zealand Minister of Agriculture, Mr Brian Talboys, in reply to an article in the London 'Financial Times' by John Cherrington.

Mr Cherrington, who visited New Zealand recently, painted a gloomy picture of New Zealand agriculture and urged that farming would have to be subsidised. Mr Cherrington added, 'An outstanding trait of the New Zealand character is a stubborn refusal to face the facts of modern economic life.'

Mr Talboys said 'Mr Cherrington's attitude toward our farming and marketing policies amazed me. He seems to take offence at our resolve to continue and develop as efficient producers of pastoral food products—our determination to earn a living by exploiting the natural advantages and the skills which we have.

'We have always been somewhat at odds with the rest of the world in that we have a farming industry that is not only determined but also capable of standing on its own feet.

'His remarks are all the more surprising when the European Economic Community seems to be coming more aware of the fundamental error of their ways of subsidising the reproduction of a commodity that is pricing itself out of the market,' said Mr Talboys.

It was not news to anyone associated with farming in New Zealand that the country was facing problems in some of its markets for dairy produce because of dumping by other suppliers.

'Our response to this problem has been a positive one: we try to find arrangements for more orderly marketing and ways of using surpluses in food aid programmes. Surely this is more sensible than engaging in a ruthless price-cutting war that in the end helps no-one. Mr Cherrington appears to advocate a doctrine of despair to which I for one do not subscribe', said Mr Talboys.

February 1969   REUTER

NFU Is Waging a Hard, Deliberate Campaign Against Food Imports

The philosophy of despair put forward by the 'Financial Times' agricultural writer John Cherrington, was a well-worn view New Zealanders have heard many times before, the General Secretary of Federated Farmers Mr J. G. Pryde said in a statement on February 14.

The General Secretary was referring to articles written by Mr Cherrington in the British press after his recent visit to New Zealand. These criticised New Zealand farmers for their 'pathological mistrust of subsidies' and their 'outdated' attitudes to 'fair play' in trade based on their efficiency as low-cost producers of food.

'Mr Cherrington, as a British farmer on an extensive scale, has, of course, a vested interest in the deliberate campaign being waged by the National Farmers' Union in Britain against food imports and hence one is compelled to suspect his motives,' Mr Pryde said.

'If New Zealand, and its farmers in particular, had taken notice of the gloomy prospects painted so frequently in the past by overseas writers and politicians, we would today be little better off than "the Falkland Islands on the grand scale" he mentions.

'I believe our stubbornness to which Mr Cherrington refers is not so much refusal to face facts of modern economic life—we are only too well aware of them—but rather a cold realisation of the forces we have to compete against. Does he expect us to throw in the sponge?'

• • •

February 1969   STRAIGHT FURROW

Straight Furrow *is the official organ of the Federated Farmers, the New Zealand farmers' union.*

The Nineteen Seventies

The 1970s started off with a return to power of the Conservatives and a new minister for JOC to write to.

Letter to Jim Prior

TO begin with let me convey to you my deepest sympathy. You are faced with the grave of any politician's ambitions; the Ministry of Agriculture. The late Lord Hudson, war-time Minister, said on learning of his appointment: 'Some enemy has done this to me'. His successors in office have all admitted the same thing; regarding it at best as a stepping stone to other and better things, as a punishment, or else just for the money.

But in your case it seems to be self-inflicted, no doubt because you are innocent of these matters, in fact you seem to me to be too nice to be anything but innocent.

You have probably been deluded by your own knowledge of practical farming. You think it must be simple to correct the obvious inadequacies of the past few dynasties by bringing your own experience to the rescue. You're in for a shock.

John Mackie, now languishing happily no doubt in the rural fastnesses of Enfield, is a most experienced and practical farmer. He entered the Ministry, admittedly as a subordinate, full of good intentions, determined to make Britain a better place to farm in. It's a sad story. I used to watch the poor fellow, purple in the face, choking over the tripe that his officials had put into his brief.

John Mackie made the same mistake that you seem to have done. He accepted office in a Ministry he knew something about. It's the last thing that any politician should do, particularly in Agriculture, where the officials' view of the farming facts of life in no way coincides with the realities of the situation. A Minister's job is to defend his officials in public, and take the blame for them, whatever nonsense they perpetrate.

You will have a brief honeymoon period. Farmers are so disgusted with the last Price Review and so pleased at the return of the Conservatives, for whom most would have voted even if they had been given £5,000 a year for life tax free by Mr Wilson, that they will be prepared to give you the benefit of the doubt for a week or so. At least until you refuse them a Special Price Review. I thought by the way that Mr Heath's reply to the request by Mr Plumb for one would have frozen the cockles of any bank manager's heart.

Then you will have to face the mass disapproval of the militants. I don't say they will be blocking off Whitehall, or showering you with eggs or paint. But you will be harangued by all their dreary propaganda. If you have ever spent an evening with Wallace Day you will know what I mean. They will soon remember that the last Minister to do them real harm was Christopher Soames, who instituted standard quantities, which the Socialists removed most of.

But I forget. You are being guided by your own policy statement, 'The Farming Future', brought out by shadow Joe. By the way, why hasn't he your job? Was his retreat from it just to give a new boy a chance, or was it simply strategic?

I can't help thinking it's the latter, because after all you are not only Minister to 400,000 farmers, but you are responsible for the food of the rest of the population; 50 million-odd. Now the policy statement proposes to raise the cost of the public's food. How are you going to reconcile the absurdity of reducing the cost of the housewives' shopping basket (if you listened to Ted on the Tele) with literally doubling the cost of the basic temperate foods at the same time?

I don't expect you to be able to be logical about these things because I have never heard a politician give a straight and reasonable answer to such a problem. But I certainly wouldn't like to be in your shoes when the massed housewives of Britain, all 20 million of them, descend on Whitehall waving their empty shopping baskets. Or leaving the babies they can no longer afford to feed on your own doorstep. No, the torch Joe has handed on to you is one I would have been happy to pass on to anyone innocent enough to grab it.

But since you are there, there are one or two things on the farming front that could do with the most immediate attention. It won't have escaped your notice that the period of Labour government has coincided with the growth of a good deal of bureaucratic fungi that simply cling to the structure of the farming industry, and do no good at all as far as anyone can see.

This is far from being the fault of the members of these bodies, but simply that they have not the power under their constitutions to do anything positive at all, either for good or ill. The Cereals Authority, the Meat and Livestock Commission, the Training Board, the Rural Development Boards and others are at best no ornament, and at worst a hindrance to the progress of the industry.

We could do with a Marketing Board both for cereals and probably for meat. In fact the absence of a Cereals Board automatically places us among the second eleven of the developing countries. Something will have to be done, if indeed you bring in your levy system. How else will you be able to ensure that farmers will receive the guaranteed price in times of market self-sufficiency. As far as I understand Joe's policy there is to be no support buying, only a very low fall-back guarantee.

Still the new policy will take time, and you may be translated or go to the Lords before its chickens really come home to roost.

You may care to look at the two Rural Development Boards. The one for Wales; a country fiercely radical, even Socialist in most things, where farmers have resolutely refused to allow it to be set up. The Conservative Pennine farmers on the other hand have swallowed theirs, hook, line and sinker, which leads me to the conclusion that the Conservatives are the fosterers of Bureaucracy. Or will you disband them both?

On a final and more practical note. It won't have escaped your notice, at least if you have ever read what I have written, that our advisory services are some of the worst in the world.

The staff as individuals are excellent, but the organisation is just frightful, the channel of communications between the Research Council, the NAAS and farmers is suffering from acute constipation at the bottom, and marked indigestion higher up. Most of the money is wasted in irrelevant research because no one has set out what is really needed. If you fail at all else, if you only succeed in making our advisory services as good as those of the Irish Republic or New Zealand you will deserve the long time thanks of the industry. The rest of Joe's policy is best left to natural forces to work out.

The best of luck to you.

June 1970   FARMER AND STOCKBREEDER

Royal Show

MY first impression of this year's Royal Show, besides the sultry heat, was quite literally shocking; car park charge up to 10s, entrance fee doubled to £2 on the first day. Why this 100 per cent rise, we asked? Never been raised for 21 years, they said. Is the society in such financial trouble? No, it's just to keep the crowds out.

To-day, the first day, should be for the elite visitor. A thousand people from 50 countries have accepted tickets so they should be given first place at the manufacturers' stands and not be trodden underfoot by hordes of lolly-sucking schoolchildren. That may be all right for foreigners but home farmers like myself are suffering a squeeze, so the machinery lines are of no real commercial interest.

But the expenditure at the gate has to be recouped somehow. Fortunately one can display interest without actually signing an order form and hopeful expectation is a wonderful opener of the drinks cabinets. After gin with an agricultural paper, a cattle breeding society, three manufacturers and a seedsman, I felt the need of shade.

Under the same tree was a falconer of Hungarian origin dressed in a leather jerkin and hat decorated with hundreds of badges. He told me that his birds came from North Africa and the Middle East. None from England because the Royal Society for the Prevention of Cruelty to Animals has instituted legislation to prevent one taking and training the home-bred article. What did he chase with them? Partridges and pigeons. Did he ever catch any? Well, very, very seldom, he said.

On to lunch with a charming German lady who asked me what the Royal Show was and who ran it, and why. Was it the farmers? Well, some farmers. But then she said, why no traditional costumes. In Germany at similar functions everybody dresses in the appropriate costume. I explained that tradition used to mean a bowler hat at the Royal Show but was now discarded in favour of hatless democracy, and, for the first time in my memory, shirt sleeves as well. She said it was fine with her, but tradition, she declared, was something to hang on to and to fight for. For the sake of our future membership of the Common Market, I had to agree.

Paused briefly by the judging rings but found the results completely incomprehensible. Years ago judging was simply on looks but now it's been complicated by such things as milk yields, conversion rate of feed, weight for age and the like. But who would pick a beauty queen for her brains?

Finally to a Press conference. No overseas sales announced to-day. The manufacturers' representatives were very guarded about supporting the Show much longer. They felt that manufacturers needed results in terms of cash for their expenditure here. The attendance, we were told, was slightly down, but they were getting more members at the gate on a 20 per cent discount.

To-morrow, it will only cost a quid to come in and it may be cool enough to perambulate the Show in comfort and so gain a more logical view of this shop window of the agricultural industry.

July 1970   FINANCIAL TIMES

Conservation versus Farming

CONSERVATION and anti-pollution are the twin crusades of the 1970s and farming is fast catching up with industry as being public enemy number one. In some cases there is some truth in the accusation that farmers both pollute their surroundings and upset the balance of nature, which is what I imagine the conservationists to be anxious to preserve.

By pollution, as I understand it, is meant creating circumstances under which human life becomes impossible through poisoning of atmosphere or food, or the prevention of plant growth. On this score, farmers in Britain have something to answer for but not as much as is thought.

There are bad cases of pollution of streams or the atmosphere by effluent from pig and poultry flocks or from silage, particularly in industrial areas. But the damage here is more to human sensibility than to health: it is, after all, not necessary to human survival that there should be fish in the rivers.

There are also safeguards. Local authorities and river Boards have the power—even if in some cases they don't have the will—to control the effluent that farmers allow to come into their rivers. Where these powers are exercised, they are quite effective. Human and industrial waste disposal has ruined far more rivers than farming ever has.

Otherwise there is little evidence in Britain of health hazards from farming. There is no suggestion that the lakes and rivers of England will suffer the blight of lakes Erie and Michigan, which are said to be so rich in nitrogen from excess run-off from farms, that the consequent growth of plant life has exhausted the oxygen on which the fish depend and killed them.

In this instance there is some conflict. Many say that farmers are not to blame, but that sewage, even purified sewage from the big cities, has exactly the same effect.

On the question of the preservation of wild species, hypocrisy is absolutely rampant. Myxomatosis was the greatest single boon that farming has enjoyed over the last few decades, but the general public opinion has been that it was a dreadful thing to have happened. The fact was that the rabbit population had got completely out of hand because its main enemies, stoats, weasels, etc., had been ruthlessly stamped out by keepers anxious to increase the stock of game birds to be shot for sport. At the same time foxes, which are the worst destroyers of game birds extant, are allowed to survive to provide sport for others.

The present animal plague at the moment is the wood-pigeon, which flourishes unchecked in all well-keepered districts because it has no enemy left. I have no objection at all to field or blood sports, but I give no credit to conservation schemes that encourage one species at the expense of all the rest.

The conflict between the conservationists and farmers is simply that between those who make their living off the land and those who want to enjoy the countryside and its landscape. I have often thought that the average townsman still sees the country as in a picture by Constable or Landseer. Either all trees, hedges and thatched cottages, or else majestic bog and mountain, with deer.

These romantic pictures were factual a couple of hundred years ago, but nothing in the countryside stands still. Land—even Scottish mountains—has to be put to economic use if its owners are to survive, and what is more important, provide food for increasing populations. I don't as a farmer blame local authorities or conservationists for attempting to put more and more restraints on farmers who want to move hedges, cut down trees and otherwise upset a preconceived picture of what the countryside should look like. In this modern age anyone is entitled to get as much as he can for nothing, for there is never any suggestion that any of this interference with farmers' businesses should be paid for. But this is a cause for conflict.

And this is bound to be aggravated by the growth of population, leisure and motor cars. A sensible solution would be to set aside areas for recreation pure and simple. The present national parks and areas of outstanding natural beauty are practically useless for this purpose, as most of them are owned and occupied by people trying to farm them in various ways.

Britain is far behind Holland in this respect. There, planning of land for use in farming, housing and recreation is coordinated, and areas taken for recreation are paid for through their taxes by those who enjoy them. It's time we had a similar sensible solution here.

October 1970   FINANCIAL TIMES

Vagaries of the Weather

JUNE

THE drought which was only sporadically broken by very local thunderstorms last week has now lasted three or four weeks over most of England and Wales. This is a short period by comparison with droughts in other parts of the world. But because in Britain every human and agricultural activity seems to be based on the principle that it rains at all times of the year, any deviation from this norm soon brings an emergency, with water rationing in the towns and bare pastures and dried out crops on the farms.

There is in consequence very little in the way of irrigation systems of the sort that have to be adopted in the hotter countries to make sure of any crops at all. Nor have farmers adopted systems that are forced on dry land farmers in other parts of the world, in which sparse crops are the norm rather than the exception.

Most of our farming is dependent on what might be called surface rainfall; only small areas have the advantage of a high water table which can supply the moisture needed for constant growth throughout the summer. Another factor is the extent of the effect of evaporation on the water already present at the time of growth, starting in the spring. There is very little evaporation during the winter; the land in many cases remains sodden until the late spring, especially if drainage is not too good

A good drainage system can be either artificial, in that at some time the land has been underlaid with pipes, or the soil and the subsoil can be naturally free draining. Drainage can work two ways. Moisture flows down when in excess, and at times of drought can rise again through capillary action, and be available to the growing crop. At the same time a free draining soil allows the passage of the plant roots, so that they can seek moisture at the depth at which it is available.

Farmers can help these natural processes by means of cultivating techniques. Broadly speaking, a seed bed that is fine, to a good depth, will retain moisture much better than one that is lumpy and irregular. The use of the roller after the crop is sown will reduce the area of soil open to the atmosphere.

Because of these variations in British soil conditions, which change with bewildering rapidity from parish to parish, it is impossible to make an accurate assessment of the effects of the present drought period. This has lasted in the South for nearly a month without measurable rain of any significance. But certain broad generalisations can be laid down.

This last spring was late and rather wet, which meant that many farmers on the heavier clay lands were late in getting their spring corn planted. I travelled across southern England to Norfolk in late May, and it was most significant that on the heavier lands the barley crops were only just through the ground, while those on the light sands of Norfolk, and the Hampshire and Wiltshire chalks, were looking extremely well.

It is these late sown crops that are suffering particularly badly at this moment, as their very sparseness denies the soil the cover against evaporation that a heavy crop provides. Also the very fact of hot weather—and the last few weeks have been very warm indeed for late May and June—accelerates the maturing processes. This could lead in the end to very premature ripening, with a consequent loss of yield.

The heavier crops on the lighter soils are more promising, especially those on the chalk farms, because the chalk subsoil is said to act like a sponge, absorbing the moisture in excess and releasing it as required. Sandy land does not have this characteristic to anything like the same extent.

Until now I have been talking of the spring-sown crops—mainly barley, with some wheat and oats which represent about two-thirds of the cereal acreage. Winter wheat can survive this sort of weather well, since its roots are deep and it makes the most of its root and leaf growth before the longest day. It is almost unaffected by a lack of rain once it has made this essential development.

Grassland is different. After the late spring, growth on well fertilised pastures was very rapid, and many farmers have secured good crops of silage and some hay. The emphasis, though, is on the quality of the material, rather than the weight. The best silage, of high dry matter content, is made when the sun shines, and this year has been very good indeed. The hay now being baled is green and looks just like real dried grass. It will be much appreciated by the stock next winter, when it will undoubtedly have to be strictly rationed.

But those farmers like myself who give their stock a free run of their pastures at a time of the first growth in the spring, have been badly caught. The fields I have closed up for hay have made no growth at all in the past three weeks, while at the same time the pastures on which the sheep and cattle are feeding are being eaten down to the roots.

This of itself is no bad thing. Within reason grazing livestock thrive best on short commons, as long as the weather is dry and warm. My lambs are doing particularly well at present, probably because there is no room for the parasitic worms to thrive on the dry herbage, and the content of the leaf is higher in feed value than if it were lush and wet.

Dairy cows are a rather different case. They require plenty of good lush grass to ensure milk production, and they have now eaten off most of the first flush of spring growth. That which has followed is mostly sparse and running to seed heads. This drastically lowers the milking potential and at the same time effectively prevents regrowth for a while.

At the moment then, this summer's farming prospects are in the balance. If the drought continues for much longer, together with this great heat, crops will be very light apart from winter wheat, and sugar beet, too, will be affected. Livestock farmers will also face great difficulties because, unless there is adequate rain, all significant pasture growth will stop in two or three weeks.

If, on the other hand, there is a reversal to normal rainfall, no harm will be done. It is an unpredictable situation, which farmers are trained to accept, because they have no alternative.

JULY

A FORTNIGHT ago I was almost suicidally depressed. There had been no rain for about five weeks, pastures were burning up badly; barley was hardly growing at all, only the deep-rooted winter wheat was showing any sign of promise of a good harvest. The sheep looked well, but I knew that it wouldn't be long before the ewes lost their milk, and then the lambs would begin to lose their bloom.

The only consolation was that most of my neighbours were in the same straits. In time of trouble it is always best to be one of a crowd, and not just on one's own, otherwise it looks as if it's all your fault.

The rain, when it came, was rather spasmodic and very local, but it has been enough to green up the pastures which are now looking like green billiards tables, and not brown ones, and the sheep do look as if they have had something to eat. I have been very worried and was prepared to sell every killable lamb, however light, had it not rained. This slaughter of the innocents would have earned me a great deal less than they would if kept to maturity, but the prospect of having a thousand or more thin lambs wandering around my empty fields eating expensive concentrates was more than I could bear.

I knew that the drought had been general over the South of England and this would mean that there would be few buyers for my sheep to fatten on other pastures. It's often the case that the store lambs I sell come to more money than the fat ones sold earlier in the season. The trade, if there had been a trade, would have been very bad indeed. The trouble with the sheep section is that one is so much at the risk of the weather and the quality of the pasture. Concentrates are available but they are expensive and sheep are very bad converters of grain into flesh.

The barley outlook was also very dismal. A good season for barley would be one where the weather until mid-June is warm and humid so that the plant tillers well and produces a lot of leaf. And then for there to be good, hot sunshine thereafter.

There was no lush growth this year, and the crop was so thin that there was no shade to stop the ground being dried out, and the ears emerged only slowly from the straw. This is an important stage in the plant's development. In a good season the barley ears come well clear of the sheath, six inches to a foot above the nearest leaf. In a really bad season I have noticed that the ears never quite clear the straw, the grain fails to swell and the result is a very bad harvest indeed.

A good, thick crop of barley will show all the ears nicely necked over and the straw is so thick that it is a job to walk through. This thickness has another advantage; when ripe, barley straw tends to break up very badly. If the straw is thick it will form a mat that will keep the ears off the ground until they can be harvested. A thin crop provides no support, and I fear if harvesting is delayed through bad weather, losses could be considerable.

The only advantage of this year's short crop is that it is unlikely to be laid flat at this stage as it so often is when too thick and green. As long as it will stand above the combine knife there will be a harvest of sorts.

Wheat on the other hand looks very well everywhere I have been. It is a deep rooted plant and can stand a great deal of drought as it does most of its development during the early spring, before the moisture has been evaporated. In spite of its apparent promise it is still very much at risk of the weather. If July turns cold and damp the maturity of the grain can be hampered by a variety of rusts and other diseases. The sunshine of 1969 was perfect, and I had the best wheat yield I have ever had. The next six weeks is crucial to the success of the crop.

The position up to now is like this. There has been enough rain to keep the stock going and, more important still, grass is growing well in the West of England where many of my store lambs will have to be sold so the danger of forced sales is no longer as great as I feared at one time.

I can now bear to go and look at my barley fields again without an attack of the horrors. Ear emergence is almost complete and the plant population is certainly high. Straw is still very short but there is a chance that the crop will yield an average return, perhaps 30 cwts an acre, but only a chance. Last year it was nearly 40. Two fields of rye grass for seed look very well indeed. But this is a real gamblers' crop, completely dependent on the weather and can return nothing from £80 an acre.

However the suspense won't last much longer. Harvest should be over in about eight weeks for better or worse and after a brief relaxation I shall be starting the same cliff-hanging cycle again. I never learn.

NOVEMBER

IT is worth putting on record that this autumn has been one of the best that I can remember. At the beginning of September I had finished harvest with the worst barley yield for a long time, one of the best for wheat, very little hay and only enough straw to bed the pigs. Grass hadn't finished recovering from the drought and I had nearly a thousand lambs on hand and a handful of cattle.

I had been reducing my store cattle numbers since mid-summer, when I saw that hay was scarce to the point of non-existence. Far better to let someone else carry them through the winter at great expense; so they went to an optimist and I kept the money. My forethought seemed justified until the mini price review in October, which gave a tremendous spurt to the store trade.

Had I kept them I might have made more money of them, but I was not to know—such was the security on this occasion—that Mr Prior was going to be so generous. Perhaps he didn't know himself until the event. But even another 20s a live hundredweight is only £9 per beast, and would hardly meet the extra cost of hay and grain.

There is always an argument about costing winter feed. Some economists argue that supplies grown on one's own farm should be charged at production cost, others that market prices should be taken as the criterion. I incline to this latter view because when feeding hay or barley grown on the farm it's as well to know just what it would make if sold. If to fatten your stock at a profit you have to use grain at less than its market price, there is something wrong with your fattening system.

I had also liquidated my lambs by the first week of November. Some had fattened on grass, the remainder on a field of rape hired from a neighbour. The trade has been rather slow partly because the French had stopped imports on October 1, and because of heavy selling by farmers fearful of the winter. But prices, helped by the subsidy, were quite good, and I was not forced to feed any expensive concentrates. Less than 100 had to be sold as stores for other farmers to fatten in the West of England, where they make a speciality of winter fattening.

This clearance of cattle and lambs meant that the ewes have had ample grass to graze and it has been of exceptional quality and quantity. They have been mated in an improving condition which, according to the pundits, should mean a heavy drop of lambs next March. Most farmers try to achieve this condition in their ewes, but it is not easy in the average autumn as the grass is often losing its goodness. This time the combination of sufficient moisture for growth with generally dry land has been just right. I have never seen the flock look better.

Arable work is very forward, and it's likely that a record wheat crop is in sight for next year. But the only certainty about this is the acreage. Wheat yield depends on the health of the crop in the months before harvest and there are certain disquieting indications that the present farmers' optimism in wheat plantings may be misplaced.

The last two wheat harvests in the south have been among the best I have ever known, healthy, heavy crops. We have had good crops before but never in succession and there is every chance that if next year we have the usual pattern of the English summer there will be a lot of very disappointed growers. The trouble is that the success of the last two years had blinded us to the dangers of breaking the traditional rotation rules that wheat should be grown only on a wheat entry; that is, after a succession of crops which effectively breaks the disease cycle.

Much of the wheat planted this time has transgressed to the extent that many farms have got completely out of any sense of rotation, and might take a long time to get in order again. The success of the last two years had not been because of any improvement in variety or disease control, but simply because the weather suited the crop. However, I cannot talk. I have transgressed as badly as the rest, but I have a guilty conscience about it which younger farmers may not feel.

The heavy rains of the last week or so have done the power of good. A lot of the early wheat had been planted in very dry ground and had not germinated too well. Now it has caught on and growing fast. The ewes seem to have enough grass to keep them going until the snow, and there is just enough hay I think to manage through the winter.

Most other farmers have been making the same arrangements, and dairy farmers have been saving at least three or more weeks' winter feed.

We shall get through the winter all right in spite of the light hay and silage crop if there is an early spring. And after the last two very late springs, this is surely not an unreasonable expectation.

1970 FINANCIAL TIMES

Farewell to F and S: Welcome to BFSB

THIS is the last article I shall write for *Farmer and Stockbreeder* in its present form. I began as a regular contributor in 1958 and in the 13 years that have followed I have written, give or take a few lost through strikes, illness or travelling abroad, about 330 pieces. That makes a total of something over 400,000 words. The mind boggles!

I had actually started to write at the end of the war. Something that was said by Sir George Stapledon angered me so much that I felt impelled to write a letter to an editor. I said that when talking about the value of a grass break Sir George was talking nonsense. Unless he put down in clear terms the financial benefit the grass ley would provide, ley farming was a waste of time and money—a view I hold just as strongly today.

This effusion took me about half an hour on a typewriter that had cost £5 10s years before. The editor of *Farmers Weekly* sent me a cheque for £7 7s. This I thought was terrific: here was I with a total investment of £5, making a profit of 140 per cent on my capital for the cost of half-an-hour's time—time which I would otherwise probably have spent reading, washing up, gardening or looking after the children.

I have never done any of the last three since. You see, once you can justify to your domestic critics when either reading or hitting a typewriter you're gainfully employed, eking out the penury of a farming existence, criticisms tend to be muted.

Mind you, success, such as it is, did not come overnight, nor for that matter was I continually bombarding editors with copy for them to reject, although I have had my share of that disappointment. My main writing efforts for the next few years were concerned with securing a measure of security for tenant farmers.

I had had the experience of being turned out at a year's notice from two farms within five years; and the second time I had to wait a number of years for my out-going valuation. I was, at the time of this campaign, farming as a tenant something like 1,500 acres. Although some of the land was leased, I felt that my whole farming future was completely at the whim of a landlord.

I propagandized both through the National Farmers' Union and the farming Press for a change in the law, which granted an evicted tenant only the maximum compensation of two years' rent. It wasn't easy to get farmers' support for this. Many of them were still frightened of upsetting their landlord. But the editors of both farming papers gave me plenty of space, and space also to my supporters and opponents of whom there were a number.

While the 1947 Act was being discussed I discovered that the NFU was not asking for full security, only for an increase in the compensation payable. I didn't think this was enough, nor did my supporters who were gaining in numbers by this time. So we redoubled the propaganda in letters, and also approached the politicians concerned. On being asked what would satisfy us, I replied on behalf of my friends that nothing less than full security would, and to everybody's surprise this was written into the Bill.

There are several lessons in this. In the first place it is

essential, I think, to have a free Press, which the farming papers I am glad to say have always provided. It also demonstrated that reasoned arguments persistently presented would eventually convince people of their validity. It also showed that in negotiation you don't get anywhere by being moderate in your demands at the outset. You should always ask for rather more than the very best you can hope for and then you have got something to give way on.

It also demonstrates to me that it pays to disregard short-term considerations when pressing a case of vital importance. I was a tenant farmer at the time and some of my remarks about landlords may not always have been in the best of taste and certainly weren't tactful. Many suggested that I might suffer for my activities. I didn't; and I have always thought that as long as one sticks to attacking policies and even the effectiveness of those carrying out those policies it is perfectly fair within the mechanism of democratic progress.

It also lays one open to similar treatment from the other side, but I don't think that matters a bit. The only alternative to progress by argument is progress by the bomb which in the end is, as they say, counter-productive.

I have worked under a number of editors. All of them demonstrated an extreme scepticism which is probably the essential part of their stock in trade. Without it they would be at the mercy of every crank with an eye to publicity. As one said once, looking hard at me, 'Only really persistent cranks get on to my pages'.

But I would like to pay tribute to the help the editors and proprietors of *Farmer and Stockbreeder* have given me over the years and to the opportunities which I have had through this association to travel and also to broaden my writing interests. *Farmer and Stockbreeder* is a considerable paper in the eyes of overseas farmers, and mention of its name opened doors to me, particularly in my early travelling days, which I might have had difficulty in opening in any other way.

And now, to my sorrow, the *Stockbreeder* is dying, to be born again like some Phoenix in partnership with the *British Farmer*. I have been asked to continue writing for the new publication. I am happy to do so. I have always been accustomed to writing for independent papers which give their contributors freedom to report facts and express their own opinions, and the editor assures me that this will continue.

I have had differences with NFU policies and personalities in the past. I very much doubt if, even under our new President, I shall always be in agreement with his actions (or lack of them) or with those of the new Director-General.

But I think that the NFU or any democratic organisation of this sort, should provide a forum in which expressions of other than the official line can be ventilated. The new proposals for streamlining the organisation and cutting down the number of the council meetings makes the need for an active forum of debate even more essential than it was before.

The new *British Farmer and Stockbreeder* could, and should, become that medium. Every farmer should belong to the Union whether he agrees with its policies or not. Some who don't claim that their reason is they don't feel that the Union caters enough for minorities. This is perfectly true. But the way to get this altered is not to just sit back and sulk but to join the Union, and contribute to its debates as persistently and as bloody-mindedly as I did in my early days. I might not have achieved much, but I have certainly enjoyed it all.

Properly directed the *British Farmer and Stockbreeder* could make a splendid forum.

February 1971   FARMER AND STOCKBREEDER

Welcome EEC

NOW that the die appears to be cast I should like to make my own position clear on the Common Market. I was at one time completely against the idea. Government from Brussels at the hands of the Commission was likely to be so bureaucratically hidebound that I shuddered at the thought of my future being in the hands of civil servants even more uncontrollable than our own.

I have also a deep suspicion of idealists, and for a long time the starry-eyed were in command of things. Anyone, just anyone, who mattered was in favour of entry, and for no better reason than that the EEC was there, was new, and therefore better. But this is changing. Instead of being an idealistic outward-looking collection of states, the EEC has become an inward-looking, self-centred customs union, seeking only the material advantage of its members.

Power at the centre has obviously been lost. The recent currency changes when Germany and Holland revalued were decided evidence that, whatever the Commission, or even the majority of members of the Six felt, a country could go its own way. This is fine. It's a much better basis for building European unity than any number of fine phrases and pie-in-the-sky schemes.

Therefore I am in favour of joining. Not just on the basis of the girl about to be raped who was advised to lie back and enjoy it, but because once all idealistic notions have been washed out there remains a much better basis for evolving a workable system of European unity. From the lowest common denominator of selfishness up, rather than from the top down.

Our Government would be much better advised in its propaganda for joining if it pointed out the real truth of this, instead of underlining to all and sundry the prospective benefits to fit any particular case.

I can't see any advantage, for instance, for the motor industry in joining a community where there are already plenty of car manufacturers. The same goes for nearly everything else in industry, particularly when all our exports to the Six have to go by the bottleneck of sea transport. Practically all propaganda in favour is specious, including that of the Minister of Agriculture when he promises better things.

As a grain grower I shall enjoy the extra prices, anything from £10 per ton upwards for the main cereals. But there is bound to be a catch somewhere, if only that inflation will have caught up with our lower costs and the removal of the fertiliser subsidy and probably leave the margins just as at present. I have a sense of foreboding about this, in any case.

Grain is the only EEC farm product that is priced out of line. High grain prices are definitely putting much of French farming out of balance to the detriment of the livestock side, particularly pigs and poultry, and the same applies elsewhere. As civilisation advances, so people eat less starch and more animal products, therefore in all the Community there will be pressure for lower feedingstuff prices.

There is another very cogent warning sign. There is a world shortage of dairy products at present, one that I think will endure, because people are getting tired of milking cows. There is a slight beef shortage which may not go on much longer. The potential for increased beef production in countries like the Argentine is immense. The decline in output there has been largely caused by lack of investment due to persistently low prices. This may take some time to alter, but the potential is very much there, as it is in Europe in places like Ireland.

But the recent high prices have only made a tiny dent in the export surpluses of grain, particularly of wheat. And behind the surpluses is the fact that a combination of quotas and low prices is keeping hundreds of millions of acres of cropping land out of production. The only country in the Six which is really interested nationally in a high grain price is France; all the rest are, like ourselves, net importers with huge industrial populations wanting proteins.

I don't think grain growing is necessarily going to be sold down the river, but a persistently high level of grain prices will come to look stupid in the general context of the economy of the ten countries. And the eventual outcome of this obvious stupidity might well cost us dear, at least those of us who think corn growing will enter a golden age.

I don't know if I shall live long enough to see it happen, but already there are people in prominent positions in all these countries who are beginning to talk. Just as the agitators did at the time of the repeal of the Corn Laws, more than a century ago.

Meanwhile I think it's time that the NFU got active. It's no good waiting on events, as it seems to be doing—merely deploring the vagueness and lack of consultation with Brussels and the Government.

I may, of course, be doing Mr Plumb and his advisers an injustice; they may be pressuring Mr Prior in private for information, for assurances. But pressure by farmers on their own governments is a fact of life in the Six. Avoiding these sorts of pressures is Mr Prior's number one priority if he can get away with it. And it will, of course, be the same with his successors in title.

The related subject to which answers are required is present and future marketing. We have had a doubtful OK for the continuation of the Milk Marketing Board. We should have a certainty. Then what about potatoes? There is no system like ours in the present Six. There is no acreage quota and a pooling of subsidy between Government and farmers.

Then there is the vexed question of what to do about pig meat and poultry products. The only protection in the Community is a support buying system for pig meat pitched *below* the ascertained cost of production; plus, of course, protection from imports from outside the Community, which is of doubtful value as both these items are likely to be in overall surplus.

There will be intervention buying for cereals, beef, milk products and so on—but who is going to do this?

All these things will have to be sorted out and decided within the next five or six years. The NFU will have to be involved to the limit in all that is done, otherwise things very much to our disadvantage could be perpetrated.

In one particular respect they are likely to be disappointed. Their insistence on an Annual Review is a good thing in itself, and French farmers have been trying to get the same sort of system working with their present Minister, M. Cointat. But after his Prime Minister had agreed, M. Cointat refused to countenance any effective action at all.

No wonder French farm leaders are fearful of handing too much responsibility over to Brussels, and are redoubling their pressures on their own politicians.

So in the murky Community of Ten there will be room for every trick and blackmail, for every vice that has sabotaged the prospective unity of mankind since the attempted building of the Tower of Babel.

It won't be a pretty century or so until real unity is achieved. But it's better than making war, which is why I am hesitantly in favour.

July 1971   BRITISH FARMER AND STOCKBREEDER

The World of Plenty

HARDLY a week goes by without a prophecy of imminent disaster for the human race. If we are not to be poisoned by environmental pollution, we shall be starved through exhaustion of the soil, and if by some superhuman achievement of agricultural science food production looks like keeping pace with population growth, failure of water supplies will frustrate its success. After reading all this, and viewing it on countless television programmes, the human species might just welcome all-out atomic war as an acceptable alternative.

It is possible, indeed probable, that so alarmed shall we become that what the surgeons call heroic measures may be taken to control the growth of populations. One can foresee a time when the birth rate may be controlled by compulsory sterilisation or abortion, just as in some countries plague sufferers used to be killed to prevent the spread of infection. I would not for one minute deny the seriousness of the population explosion, but so far as food is concerned there are enough resources in the world to feed two or three times the present population.

The fact that they are not being adequately fed is a human, not a natural deficiency. If countries fail to provide satisfactory conditions for food production and distribution, it is usually the fault of the government concerned—not because of erosion, or the failure of soil structure or crop or animal disease; it is simply because farmers in those areas have not the resources to make the best use of their land. The fact is, and it has been borne out by almost every practical agricultural scientist I have met, that most of the cultivatable world is either half farmed or not farmed at all.

Scientists, of course, cover a wide spectrum. At one extreme are the pessimists like Georg Borgstrom, who believe that soil structure is breaking down and that the end of the world is in sight, and at the other are the superoptimists like Norman Borlaug, the Nobel Prize winner and originator of the 'Green Revolution', who believe that modern techniques will solve everything lacking in food production. There are quite a few scientists of the Borgstrom school, but their pessimism is contradicted by the fact that in Western Europe, where the soil has been farmed with an ever increasing degree of intensification for the last 2,000 years, crop yields are consistently rising.

Soil structure is an emotive term, and means I suppose that balance between organic—that is vegetative—matter in the soil, and inorganic or mineral material. Good farming can enable crops to be grown under a wide variety of soil conditions. I have seen equally good crops of fruit and vegetables on irrigated deserts in California and the Middle East as in the most fertile areas of the world, like the Po Valley in Italy for instance.

At Rothamsted Agricultural Research station, experiments have shown that organic matter in the soil has hardly varied through 100 years of continuous cereal cropping. In Mexico, on the slopes of Popocatépetl, where continuous growing of maize has lasted for 8,000 years, yields have trebled over the last few years, thanks to the introduction of hybrid seeds and new techniques of peasant farming.

Crops will not grow without water, of course, but there is little evidence to show that water supplies in general are failing. Areas where water was always short are still lacking; elsewhere enormous amounts are wasted. Israel utilises 95 per cent of all water resources—Britain something like 5 per cent of her rainfall. In South America the enormous river systems of the Amazon, Parana and Orinoco run largely to waste.

It is quite true that in some heavily populated countries like Britain, sewage and industrial pollution of rivers is a problem, but this can be overcome by modern methods. The Secretary of the Environment recently announced a £1,300m. scheme to clean up the rivers. It could be that some food production would have to move to areas of land with access to water, but land suitable for intensive farming exists within reach of all these river systems.

Nor should lack of fertilisers be a bar. There are at present ample supplies of phosphate and potash. If proper methods of recovery were used these elements could be retrieved from the waste products that flow into the lakes and seas. Nitrogen is at present costly to make from existing fuel systems, but atomic power will probably make it cheaper and in any case there are plants, clovers and other legumes which produce a surplus of nitrogen for use in the next crop. It is significant that in New Zealand, where grass land production is the highest in the world, no artificial nitrogen is used at all.

It is true that intensive farming aggravates the effects of crop and animal diseases, but in fact their incidence is no more than it ever has been. There is an old book, dating from the 16th century, by one Thomas Tusser. In it he describes a whole variety of ills that affect a farmer's crops and stock, together with the cures he recommends. When I started farming 40 years ago his remedies were still popular, it is only in the last 25 years that we have been able to control these diseases satisfactorily by scientific means.

Such controls have entailed the use of drugs and chemicals, which has alarmed the conservationists' lobby—it seems to be more concerned about the lives of a few birds and animals than with those of the human population. In spite of 'Silent Spring' and other tracts there is no evidence of human and almost as little of animal harm through the use of these materials; indeed it's all to the contrary. Without them untold millions would have died.

Alarmists, while conceding that cereals may be produced in abundance, point out that mankind also needs protein. This is true, but protein is also available. In Peru alone 12m. tons of fish are turned into animal feed every year. This could, with modern refining, make an equally acceptable human protein supplement.

Those who object to my thesis seem to be activated by considerations other than feeding the world population. I met during the course of a recent journey through South America individuals in positions of some power in the Land Reform movement who considered Borlaug's 'Green Revolution' a disaster for mankind as it depended to some extent on a high cost input system of fertilisers, etc., for its success and thus perpetuated the capitalist system. That the Chinese have apparently adopted these techniques without compromising their political faith cuts no ice with them.

A serious obstacle is the insistence of the developed areas, notably the EEC and US, on encouraging their own agriculture while denying the undeveloped the resources for their own progress in the form of markets. There is no virtue in the giving of foodstuffs to countries which could probably perfectly well produce their own given sufficient help.

The biggest problem, of course, is the cost, which would be considerable. But set against what the world is at present spending on armaments it would not be very big. It would also require a massive change of mind among individuals and governments. A first step could be the liquidation of the Food and Agriculture Organisation, which has provided many scientists with comfortable jobs over the past 25 years on the proposition that mankind was bound to starve anyway, and its replacement with a body with a more positive approach.

Nothing I have said here should detract from the appalling consequences of the social problems of over-population. But at the same time it must be obvious that as a first step to solving them, adequate agricultural development is more than desirable—it is essential.

April 1972   FINANCIAL TIMES

New Zealand Lamb

WHY has New Zealand lamb been sold so cheaply in Britain? It's very difficult to give a categorical answer to this. When questioned on the subject, wholesalers, importers and retail butchers all claim that the trade is carried on in a completely free market atmosphere, and that the prices achieved have been a fair reflection of the demand.

It's probable though that what might be called the free flow of supply and demand is being influenced by the special interests operating in this trade.

The background is that until very recently (the last couple of months in fact), the wholesale price of NZ No. 2s has been regularly between 5 and 10 new pence a lb cheaper than comparable English carcases. Except for about four months in the summer, English lamb is hardly a comparable article, being what you call hogget and much heavier. The retail price is difficult to establish, but generally speaking the retail price difference between English and NZ legs, has been little more than 2 to 3 pence a lb.

This shows that NZ lamb is a most valuable purchase for the retail butcher, being a means by which he can cut the average price of his meat purchases and increase his average margin because this price differential is nearly always constant.

The reason for this seems to be that NZ lamb is badly sold in spite of its general excellence, and this demonstrates in no uncertain terms that excellence and good grading is not enough. Any selling policy must have teeth.

Let me explain from my own experience. I produce the best part of 2,000 fat lambs annually, and the best buyer of quality lamb in England is undoubtedly Sainsbury's, the big food store.

To sell to one of Sainsbury's buyers used to be thought the height of any farmer's ambitions. However, I found that while Sainsbury always insisted on the highest quality, they were always trying to push down the price. One of the arguments they always used was that the Smithfield price was falling.

I got fed up with this sort of niggling and made inquiries. I got into my car and visited a number of independent small wholesalers, most of whom had different requirements for their trade. I found that among these people Smithfield is a dirty word, and represented to them the sort of place to which parcels of meat were sent if they were unsaleable in hot weather.

This is a slight overstatement, but it is indeed in part the sink of the English trade. I found in fact that by shopping around I could do a lot better, and that one man's quality was not the same as another's, and I have made a lot more money as a result.

Now I'm in no way suggesting that the New Zealand farmer is in the same position as I am, with a wide choice of buyers. But he could be a lot better off than he is. And there are remedial steps that could be taken. I agree that your quality standards are high, but quality means just an extra bonus for the buyer if he does not pay any more for it.

The important thing is to have the option of withholding supplies from the market or to change buyers. I know that you have been foolish enough to let the major part of your slaughter and shipping facilities fall into alien hands. Your Meat Board, which should be looking after your interests, is merely fulfilling a promotional function which benefits the buyers rather more than it does yourselves.

Some of the major shippers have close connections with the retail trade in this country, which must make them wish to hold wholesale prices as low as possible. Prices fixed at Smithfield are usually, as far as the English trade is concerned, completely unrepresentative of what goes on in the rest of the country. Yet I gather New Zealand lamb prices are still fixed on the basis of Smithfield quotations.

I have in the course of my duties as a journalist often visited Smithfield, and I have never understood how prices are fixed by the salesmen. They are unable to explain it in terms of good basic English. In dealing with English meat they have of course to take into account the trade in markets around the country, but for imported meats they have not this criterion.

It would seem to me that the lamb importers who have a good article, frozen and so non-perishable, should be able to exploit the market pricewise a great deal more than they seem to. If they don't exact the last farthing at the wholesale stage, it would appear either that they aren't very good salesmen, or for some reason or other they wish to keep New Zealand lamb at a low price.

This must be the only explanation for the phenomenon that while NZ lamb is the first to plummet when there is a bad trade, it is the last to rise when things get better.

For instance English hogget has been priced at between 25 and 27 pence a lb since Christmas, while NZ lamb No. 2's only rose above 15p a few weeks ago. But at the same time, English lambs of up to 40 lb were making 28p, say 25 pence without the offals.

In fairness to the exporters it must be said that with purchases on schedule, they are taking risks which they attempt to minimise and they have every right to do this. But if New Zealand farmers want to get the best of the market they would have to take risks, and the risk I think should be to own the lambs up to the wholesale stage in England.

It should be possible for the NZ Meat Board or a comparable

Candidly Yours . . .

body to retain ownership of the lambs, with the importers acting as agents, together with the slaughter companies. There would undoubtedly be squeals of anguish about this, but remember that there are in England more than a thousand small-scale wholesalers, and many very large buyers who would be only too pleased to deal direct with the importer.

Of course the price fixers may have decided that this spring's rise in NZ lamb prices is going to last, and that in future pricing is going to be on a more realistic basis. I hope it is, and I hope it's being reflected in your returns now.

This article about the sale of NZ lamb to retail outlets in the UK has come from one of the *Farmer's* regular British contributors, John Cherrington, journalist and farmer. We print it as it was received in line with our policy of giving readers as many responsible views on controversial issues as possible. These views, of course, don't always coincide with our editorial convictions. We would, however, point out several facts which might not yet be fully apparent to an overseas observer, but which should be kept in mind in reading Cherrington's article.

One is that much less NZ lamb is now sold through Smithfield than formerly, and Smithfield prices (exporters say) are not now the main basis on which NZ export schedules are set.

A second point is that Cherrington's suggestion that NZ producers should have some option of withholding supplies from the market and of changing buyers, might well be qualified by the fact that the Meat Board was the nominal owner of nearly half of this year's lamb kill up to wholesale. So far the Meat Board hasn't given any indication of wanting to opt out of this kind of control over lamb marketing.

EDITOR

August 1972   NEW ZEALAND FARMER

The 85-hour Week

I ALWAYS knew that farmers were not the idle, market going, fox hunting, shooting, feather-bedded layabouts of popular fiction and now I have documentary proof of it. According to a recently published report by the Economic Development Committee for Agriculture (Little Neddy), farmers must be the hardest working section of the community. The average number of hours worked by every farmer is said to be 64 a week, with nearly half of them doing more than 70 hours. By contrast the number of hours worked by employees averaged 52. Wives though get away with 17 hours.

Dairy and livestock farmers seem the hardest worked. Half of them do more than 70 hours while of those classified as purely cropping farmers only 27 per cent do more than 70 hours. But even so, more than 70 per cent of them work more than 50 hours.

These figures take a bit of swallowing by non-agriculturists. And I cannot claim to be completely typical in that I spend a bit of time on journalism, but I average at least five days a week farming throughout the year and my experience certainly fits in with Little Neddy's findings.

This does not mean I am actively engaged in spreading dung or milking cows. But if my physical labour is being phased out, due to a combination of old age and infirmity, the pressure on my wits becomes increasingly severe. Perhaps this is because, in common with 90 per cent of all farmers, I have no vestige of agricultural qualifications, but did, for what it's worth, leave school at 17; rather older than the great majority of my fellows who left at 15 or under.

Be that as it may, my day starts at around 6 a.m. because, due to long years of rising at 4.30 a.m. to milk, I have not managed to train myself to wake any later. At 6.25 a.m. there is a farming programme on the BBC containing market reports and a comprehensive, but often alas inaccurate, weather forecast. At 6.45 the papers arrive, and I contend that no farmer with any size business can succeed without closely following the Financial Times's Farming and Raw Materials page, even though these days it's hard to find.

My men arrive at 7.30 a.m. and together we discuss the weather prospects, and also items of the 7 o'clock news or the latest gossip. Gone are the days when we waved the threat of the sack and eviction at them to drive them out into the fields. Our industrial relations are good on the whole, but rather time consuming.

Planning the day's work is a complex matter. We are dealing with living things, the soil, animals and the weather, in an environment which is constantly changing. It takes some time to decide what to do and then I retire to breakfast and then the office. Farmers are not great office workers and I am no exception.

It is perfectly possible to run a large farming business while remaining completely illiterate. Some of the most successful farmers I have known could hardly sign their names. But literacy is a must these days if only to claim the subsidies and grants.

In every office there is a telephone, and as I am buying or selling something most days of the year I spend quite a bit of time getting bids or quotations. Or perhaps I want to sow a new variety of wheat or buy another machine. I have seen it mentioned in the Press, perhaps even seen official reports of yields etc.; I have certainly had some sales propaganda about it.

But all this just awakens my interest. What is valuable is the experience of other farmers, so it takes an hour or so of telephoning to begin to make up my mind on this and that. Then the supervisory side of my job begins. Supervisory is hardly the term though, it's more akin to a doomwatch.

All farm stock, live and dead is subject to either the ills of the flesh or those of decay. Animals get ill and die; machinery wears out; even if this process isn't accelerated by maltreatment.

If I go to see how a tractor, a baler, or a combine is getting on, it's often broken down or is making noises that indicate collapse at some future time. If we are not too pressed, as in winter, it can be stopped and repaired. But if it is at some crucial time, like harvest, we usually bash on in the hope that it holds together until it rains or harvest finishes. This is a serious decision but one that has to be made frequently and is the main cause of stress, from which farmers, again according to the Neddy report, suffer an incidence three times that of their workers.

Animals need constant supervision, and not only at lambing and milking. Only a skilled stockman can note the subtle changes of health that creep gradually over a flock or herd. I employ thoroughly competent men, but there is an old saying that a master's eye is the best dung. Or is it his foot? But feet are out now. There isn't time to walk round a farm to-day, and animals are much better studied from a car or Land Rover. Concentration on animals is definitely assisted by the radio adjusted to the station of one's choice.

British farmers are often accused of spending too much time at markets and sales. But the fact is that either because of this, or in spite of it, they make better prices of what they sell than their competitors who are disciplined by co-operation of an almost religious fanaticism as are the Danes, and stock and station agents in the Antipodes.

I attend markets and sales where I seldom do more than listen attentively to the grape vine, or, as critics would call it, gossip. I can truthfully say that the few successful deals I have made originated in ideas or news picked up in these places.

Then back home for a last look round before the men go home, and then I am in charge. If the stock gets out, or a dog chases the sheep, or someone leaves a stubble fire blazing, it's my telephone that rings. I am on duty till the men come again next morning.

There is, of course, time for relaxation. A visit to other farmers, perhaps, where the ladies congregate at one end of the room and the men at another in order to talk farming, of course. What is said may not be strictly relevant to my own business, but it is all stored in the subconscious for future reference. And then home to what could be, in city terms, an early bed, but not before having walked round the farrowing sows before retiring.

The plain fact is that every waking hour I am farming, which adds up to about 17 hours a day, or 85 hours in a five-day week. Most farmers do the same or more, which must account for the fact that we don't retire easily. Some 10 per cent of all farmers are over 65 and 30 per cent over 55.

September 1972 FINANCIAL TIMES

Obsolete Farmers

WELL, we are all Europeans now, and I don't feel any the better for it. In fact, if anything I am in a considerable state of mental conflict.

I recognise the essential need for more European unity, and this was brought out most strongly in President Nixon's inauguration speech, which seemed to indicate American isolation from the problems of other nations. Because the major cause of the last war was the American withdrawal from the old League of Nations, an alternative must be provided. This of course is the Government's real reason for joining, and it's a pity they haven't been more frank about it.

That being said, I am becoming increasingly appalled by our own loss of what is called sovereignty. In most spheres of farming we are no longer free agents; even our Price Review will have to be vetted by Brussels before it is legally applicable here.

If you don't believe this, just see what has happened to the Danes. They thought that they would be clever, and adopt the full prices for grain, etc. current in the Community, and so get a big enough compensatory payment on their bacon exports to this country to relieve them of the subsidy they were paying their farmers. After three days and nights in Brussels they found that they were only going to get half the subsidy or compensatory amount they expected, and they had to remove the whole of the subsidy they paid the farmers.

There's been the hell of a row in the Danish Parliament. The Government almost fell, farmers feel betrayed. But the only mistake the Danes made was to be a small nation in a rather out-of-the-way part of Europe. The Community is a big boys' league.

130

So what?—you say. Britain is the second biggest in population, therefore she should be all right. This may be the case, unless all the others gang up against us on some particular issue. But in farming we are one of the middle-ranking member countries in terms of total output, and almost the smallest in numbers employed—coming behind France and Germany, and in some products like grain, Italy as well.

This means that when some issue comes up that divides farmers in the Community, we could find ourselves in the same sort of cart in which the Danes have found themselves, with everyone against us.

It will be no good appealing to COPA for help. This organisation represents the lowest common denominator of agreement among European farmers, and its lack of importance can be gauged by the fact that its budget hardly allows it to do anything. I don't know what other countries are paying, but the total UK contribution is apparently going to be no more than £18,000—plus, of course, the costs of representation there. The NFU alone has an income of more than £1m a year.

The real action is in the Council of Ministers, and they in their turn are under pressure from their own farmers.

Let us imagine a hypothetical case. The butter mountain is now the best part of half a million tons, and the rate at which milk production is going up is likely to double that figure within two years. Consumers in the Community, incensed by the fact that they are paying for this while at the same time eating margarine, decide that something must be done.

This 'something' might be anything from the imposition of quotas, or the provision of European liquid milk for the UK market. The solution might be any sort of compromise, but there would be every chance that it could be deleterious to ourselves, because as farmers we are in a minority in Europe, and of little further practical value to any British Government.

Let me explain. The reason we had the Agriculture Act was to ensure the continuation of the cheap food policy. Now that has been abandoned, we are of little further use. All this talk of import saving and export to the Continent is a lot of political double-talk. The only possibilities of sizeable expansion are in pig and poultry products, and these would be so demanding of imported feed that they would make economic nonsense.

It's a hard, unpalatable fact of life that we are now members of an expendable industry, in a country that has handed over its power of determination of its own affairs to a confusion of conflicting interests in Brussels. It will be as well to remember this when, in a few years time, we start abusing the President of the NFU or the Minister of Agriculture of the day.

• • •

February 1973   BRITISH FARMER AND STOCKBREEDER

The Whitehall Tapes

I WAS away while the lobbying of MP's was going on, and so missed all the excitement. But generally speaking these affairs, while making the participants feel as if they are doing something worthwhile, do nothing to change politicians' minds; or rather the minds of the civil servants who advise them.

You must know that most Ministers on entering office know nothing about the subject of their department, and very little more when they move to something else. They rely for their speeches and negotiations on briefs prepared by the permanent Civil Service. In other words, the average Minister is frequently no more than a ventriloquist's dummy unless he is authorised by his Cabinet colleagues to go against the official brief.

I am not going to say in which category any of our recent Agriculture Ministers can be placed. But having recently bugged the more important offices in Whitehall Place, I submit an edited version of what might be called the *Agricultural Tapes*.

They began on a certain day last March as the new Minister enters his office on appointment.

(Because of the tradition of Civil Service anonymity, without which the country would have been twice as efficient as it is now, I am unable to give the names of the various bureaucrats, so must name them collectively as 'B'.)

132

JOC with the Ayrshire cows in the Hosier baler—both casualties of modern farming and both of which JOC used to great effect when building his farm business in the '50s. (MERL)

JOC was always happy to do a bit of shepherding. When his sons went off to farm on their own account, he was pleased to get back to the job of picking lambs for market. (MERL)

The journalist at work. JOC never really felt comfortable in a collar and tie, but he was always happy to sit at a desk and write another article. (MERL)

Will it grow? (MERL)

JOC was a keen supporter of the Oxford Farming Conferences. At this one in the early '70s he is as relaxed as ever. (MERL)

The end of the '70s was marked by the retirement of Sir Henry (now Lord) Plumb. Sir Henry asked if he might be allowed to interview JOC. John Kenyon (third from left), boss of the BBC's Farming Programme, duly obliged. The result? Judge by the smile on JOC's face! (BBC)

JOC's great relaxation was fishing. When he said he was 'going to the bank', nobody was quite sure exactly where he'd end up! (Financial Times photograph by Trevor Humphries)

JOC as he will be remembered—veteran of fifty years in farming and still smiling. (Photograph by Peter Adams)

MINISTER: Good morning all. It's nice to be back. I have, as you know, kept in touch with farming since I was last here, although leading the House and shadowing something or other while out of office. It's much like last time though, isn't it; farmers still seem to be belly-aching about something.

B: Nice to have you back, Minister. Three problems on which we need your help. The Prime Minister has given Mrs Shirley Williams twice the money we ever had to control food prices, while you are going to have less to produce with.

MINISTER: Sorry, never cross a woman politician, count me out.

B: Then we have Brussels.

MINISTER: What has Brussels got to do with it? I never believed in the place, and I thought that if I never thought about it it would go away . . . What must I do about Brussels? . . .

B: Oh that is quite simple. You just go over there in a fortnight's time with a brief which we shall give you . . . lay it on the table and go out on the town . . .

MINISTER: What will the brief say?

B: Not sure of that, but it will mean that food prices will not go up, particularly beef.

MINISTER: I understand. But what about farmers?

B: They are becoming restive . . . and you are due to see Sir Henry Plumb this afternoon.

MINISTER: What is he like?

B: A gentleman. Tries nothing underhand. Just stick to the brief we give you . . . Which subjects would you like covered?

MINISTER: What about beef and other livestock?

B: The beef position is simple. Due to the policies of previous administrations, farmers got the idea that more cattle were needed . . . There are now two million more than there were four years ago . . . At the same time, because prices rose last year the housewife refused to buy, prices fell, and farmers who had paid high prices for calves and young cattle are in trouble.

MINISTER: You mean that it's all the farmers' own fault?

B: Precisely. Those farmers who went in for beef are losing money, and those who stayed out aren't, so it's entirely their own fault.

MINISTER: Do you suggest anything should be done?

B: Nothing on end prices, because we have dismantled the deficiency payments in line with Common Market entry. However we are advised from Brussels that a calf subsidy would be allowed.

MINISTER: That does not seem very logical to me. It won't help farmers who have cattle in the pipeline.

B: Logic has no part in a Minister's duties. But it's perfectly logical to estimate that all the cattle which will be coming on the market for the next 18 months are already in the pipeline. Nothing we can do will stop them coming forward. If calves are cheapened through the subsidy it will encourage farmers to rear them, and so the supply will be kept up.

MINISTER: But what if farmers still complain?

B: Tell them that the position is under constant review, and that everything possible will be done, and that they have no need to worry.

MINISTER: Right, what about pigs?

B: Things are a little tricky here. Because of high feed costs farmers can do what they could not do with beef—they can prove that they are losing money on pigs at present. We suggest a temporary subsidy in the hope that numbers drop enough to push prices up a little, or that feed prices will fall enough to put them back in profit, preferably the latter. It's all the farmers' fault again.

MINISTER: I suppose that they produced too many.

B: Yes, no logical man would expect farmers to push up production to such an extent that prices fall to ruinous levels. The farmer's worst enemy is another farmer . . .

MINISTER: Now, why did you cut the fertiliser subsidy?

B: Your predecessors' Government talked about cutting prices *at a stroke*. For obvious reasons we would not do that. But we felt that cutting subsidies meant the same thing. The Treasury liked it.

MINISTER: Wouldn't it be sensible to subsidise fertiliser again?

B: Minister, as your predecessor said, farmers are well able to stand the full price for fertiliser, especially arable farmers; and as far as we know in Whitehall, farmers don't use them on grass—and in any case farming is prosperous on the whole.

MINISTER: How can that be?

B: It's all in figures. The net income of the industry has

risen to the highest level ever. Arable farmers have had the best year ever and we look on farming as a whole, not in its parts.

MINISTER: Does Henry Plumb agree with this?

B: He can't do otherwise. The sums are agreed by us and the NFU.

MINISTER: You mean that in spite of all this moaning they are a prosperous crowd, that they are simply crying wolf?

B: One cannot go against the irrefutable truth of statistics, especially agreed ones, and in the last resort you can stand on those.

MINISTER: That is all very well. But I have to speak to the Farmers' Club before long. What am I to say to them there?

B: Don't worry, Minister. We will provide the brief. It will be on these lines. . . . You welcome more production from Britain's soil but (and you should repeat this) it must not be produced at more than the consumer can pay.

MINISTER: But do you think farmers will accept this?

B: With respect, Minister, it's not for you to judge the acceptability of the words we put into your mouth.

MINISTER: But suppose these policies turn out to be wrong, what happens then?

B: In that case, Minister, you bear the responsibility.

May 1974   BRITISH FARMER AND STOCKBREEDER

JOC's great love (apart from farm and family, of course) was fishing, and he managed to persuade the Financial Times *that they needed a fishing correspondent!*

Salmon Fishing

THE election campaign has hardly entered my consciousness because for the last week I have surrendered to my addiction—there is no other word for it—salmon fishing. I don't know how else to explain an activity in which I stand deep in a cold rushing river stumbling from one boulder to another while waving a rod in an attempt to project feathered hooks called flies in the general direction of a fish, or where it might be.

It is usually raining; the wind is in my face, and unless I am wearing a hood and thick glasses the hooks are likely to become embedded in eyes or ears. All this at such an expense as to make the occasional salmon, which ends up in my deep freeze, as expensive as caviar.

The whole proposition is ridiculous. The salmon is a big fish with a tiny mouth. The river is enormous and the flies very small. The chances of the two meeting are remote. To make things worse the salmon only returns to the river of its birth from the sea with sex in mind. He never eats until he is spawned and returns to the sea weeks or months later. And only a tiny proportion succeed in surviving.

The only explanation I have heard as to why salmon take flies or lures at all is that the sight of a small object dancing in the current causes the fish to snap at it in an aggressive reaction. I disagree with this theory as I have watched salmon take flies from the surface as deliberately as any trout and also seen them swim round and spurn a sunken offering.

Even more inexplicable is the undoubted fact that salmon will only take at certain periods. During last week the fish in my river only obliged on Wednesday and Saturday between 11 a.m. and 1 p.m. The rest of the time the water was flogged without reward.

And flogging is the word for it. The principle of fly fishing for salmon is to cast the fly at an angle of about 60 degrees to the current which then takes it round until it is in line with the fisherman who then draws the line in and casts again. In this way all or most of the pool containing fish is covered. I should explain that salmon pools are not still waters but fast running stretches where salmon have been known to lie. Sometimes they show themselves by jumping in the air, otherwise nothing happens.

It is believed that the fish which jump won't take the fly. But true or not it's better to see them than to flog empty water although the results are usually the same. There is no real need for skill: it's all brute force and bloody ignorance.

This will be hotly disputed by experts some of whom take temperatures of both water and the air and constantly change their flies in bright light using a small dark fly and in dull a big gaudy one. During the last week in their co-operative periods the fish took all kinds of fly, outside these periods nothing would please them.

Over the years I have become cunning. I catch no more fish than when I started, but I do it more easily. My first step was to overcome the contempt of the typical Scottish ghillie. Once you let them take control you are lost, doomed to stand up to the armpits exhaustingly wielding an oversize rod and changing flies by the minute. After nearly drowning in breast waders I now never go in deeper than my knees.

Then the big rod was replaced by a 9-foot trout rod usable with one hand. Casting is a pleasure and no longer a labour of Hercules. Instead of changing flies I give the fish a choice of a large dark one and a small gaudy one on the same cast. Fish take either without any real pattern.

I don't claim that any of these departures from the conventional methods catch more fish. But they don't catch any less and they do make my addiction less laborious.

What are the pleasures? Certainly not in catching a fish which happens so seldom as to be an anti-climax; merely an interruption in the constant rhythm of casting. I have, on occasions, spent the whole of my annual fortnight without the feel of a fish. This year I caught four; three of them in the space of an hour which gave me some satisfaction and helped to fill the deep freeze but demanded nothing like the skill needed in most other forms of fishing.

The reward of salmon fishing is the total oblivion to everything else that it brings. I become a mindless automaton for the period and to be completely moronic is the best insulation against the stresses of the present day.

October 1979   FINANCIAL TIMES

Competition and the NFU

SO the NFU is backing continued EEC membership, without as yet asking farmers what they really think about it. I was present at that historic Council meeting, and then heard Sir Christopher Soames make an impassioned speech about the awful things that would happen to this country if we did not stay in. Sir Christopher was warmly applauded by an audience which had, with one or two exceptions, apparently forgotten that a dozen years ago he had probably done more harm than anyone else to British farming.

He instituted what were called then and still are, the standard quantities—whereby the amount that should be grown here was defined, and any surplus received the market and not the guaranteed price. Of course, those who over-produced did not receive this measure of discipline as individuals, because the total was pooled and everyone had to suffer for the over-production of a few.

He was a tough and uncompromising Minister, and although he is in a position of comparative powerlessness as far as interfering with our farming is concerned at the moment, he still (it seemed to me) had the same basic philosophy. When asked by Mr Vedeniapin, the former chairman of the NFU milk committee, whether British farmers would be able to fill the place left for dairy products once all New Zealand supplies had gone, even if there were surpluses in Europe, he became notably evasive. He waffled on about discipline and surplus control in a way which left me in no doubt that what he means by a Common Market is one where all producers are treated equally.

This, of course, is what a Common Market is all about. I am sure that not even the members of the NFU Council who voted for remaining in really understood that point. If they do, well and good, but they should also make it clear to the rank and file that in the last resort what comes out of Brussels is what counts, and that Whitehall in the shape of British Ministers has only a watching brief.

I know that Mr Peart and the NFU can point to some considerable successes this last year in the way of bending Community rules. But of this, two things must be said. During the period of renegotiation I felt that the European countries wanted us to remain in, and so at the same time did the British Government. In actual fact, if you study what really happened, the most the Government gained was a postponement of the full application of the CAP.

It also at the time suited the Government to keep farmers fairly sweet because food was short and looked like becoming shorter, and prices had to be kept down whatever happened. This no longer applies; the whole world food picture has changed in the last few weeks and prices could go a great deal lower on world markets. There is not the same need for expensive home production, especially as the Germans and others are at the moment prepared to send us semi-processed wheat at less than our own market price, thanks to the ridiculous compensatory amounts. In these circumstances, to talk of import-saving is to talk nonsense. It is our duty as good and loyal EEC members to take European surpluses.

I suspect that when full membership is assured, as I think it will be, this or any subsequent Government will be unlikely to give farmers the same attention as Mr Peart was enabled to do. We have already got the first fruits of the new attitude in the abolition of any guarantee for pigs after August. The pig trade is good now because prices have kept up through scarcity caused by the fall in sow numbers. Future prices will depend entirely on how far farmers go in increasing their pig herds. It will be just as simple as that. If the NFU wants to do pig farmers any good it will counsel restraint in herd building, and at the same time make sure that disease restrictions prevent foreign pork from ever coming in again.

I am also rather sorry that Sir Henry Plumb has become head of COPA while at the same time remaining President of the NFU. He was a splendid advocate *vis à vis* the Government here, and in the future pressure must be redoubled on British Governments to look after British interests. How will Sir Henry find the time to do both jobs with the application he has always put into the NFU work? And I wonder if he has ever thought of the possible conflict of interests that could arise if COPA wished to do something that was patently against British interests? I hope it's only a one-year job.

• • •

MORE than a quarter of a century ago I wanted to raise some money to buy another farm, my wife having presented me with yet another son. I was at my wits' end for the collateral with which to get the dough, and then had the brilliant idea of taking a copy of the Agriculture Act 1947 to the bank to be lodged along with the deeds and some rather dud shares. This Act, as I explained to the manager, guaranteed that anything produced from British farms would be paid for at a fair price.

He said he was sorry, but there was no precedent in the history of banking for using Acts of Parliament as security. Banks would lend only to people who had saleable items which in an emergency could be cashed. Whoever heard of an Act of Parliament being sold for cash?

This all came back to me when I heard our Minister extolling the benefits to the industry of the fact that the Government was behind our expansion, and that the White Paper on the future was a document of some value. Asked about the money to make it all possible, Mr Peart said that talks would be going on with the farmers' unions.

If talking to Ministers meant cash in the pocket, we should all be driving around in the latest Rolls-Royces, so much conversation having taken the place of policy over the last few years. But the extraordinary thing to me about the White Paper was that the Common Market was only mentioned in passing. I don't see how it is in any way possible to have an independent farming policy in the context of the Common Agricultural Policy.

I am not alone in this. Sir Christopher Soames and Pierre Lardinois have emphasised that the CAP is the guiding force, and that things we don't like about it—such as the importation of French eggs, or the disciplining of milk producers—are to be accepted as part of that common policy.

The White Paper puts emphasis on more milk. The Milk Board and the milk manufacturing industry have gone to town investing money in more manufacturing facilities so that British butter can take the place of New Zealand and other imports in due course. But if a Common Market means what it says, there is just no need for any more manufacturing here.

The Community as a whole is already more than self-sufficient in dairy products, and where else to ship the surplus than to these islands? European farmers have a right to this market, subject only to the concession made until 1977 to New Zealand. It's a cruel deception to argue, as some people do, that because British farmers are the most efficient in Europe (a phrase which needs a good deal of qualification), they will be able to compete—i.e., put other people out of business.

We have to remember that any concession from the CAP will have to be fought for by the British Minister of Agriculture of the day. The Community already has a large and expensive mountain of skimmed milk powder, a prospective butter mountain, and more cheese than it knows what to do with. The fact that British dairy farmers are more efficient than others will carry no weight with European Ministers when trying to cut down production, as they undoubtedly will before long.

Farming efficiency is not enough. It's numbers that count. In the UK, farmers are 3 per cent of the total population, the lowest of any EEC country. Elsewhere in the Community it's still substantially above this figure. This means that our vaunted efficiency is costing us dear in terms of political strength, not only here, but also in Europe. It could be said that our efficiency is our own worst enemy in this respect.

I have emphasised this situation simply because a number of farmers have told me that they are certain that the CAP is going to be the support of their future prosperity; instead of dealing with the hard-nosed British Treasury they will be part of a wider unity, joining with their brothers in Europe for a perpetual bonanza in which they can always come out on top. It's time these Pollyannas grew up. The Europeans want our market, and intend as far as possible to make it their own.

• • •

April and May 1975   BRITISH FARMER AND STOCKBREEDER

The Drought

SOME years ago I was flying from Sydney to New Zealand, and found myself sitting next to a sheep farmer from a drought-stricken area in New South Wales. There was nothing more that he could do, he told me, to stop his sheep dying. So he was going to spend a few days in New Zealand, just to enjoy the sight of grass that was green, and not a scorched memory of happier days.

Many English and Welsh farmers must be feeling the same just now, and they would have to travel a long way to find grass that is green and growing. There is some still, but, as I saw last week in the course of a journey from Hampshire to the Tweed through the Midlands and the Eastern counties and back through Cumbria and the West, it is becoming scarce. It is largely confined to the Yorkshire dales, the Cheviot valleys and the western slopes of the Pennines. Only from Scotland are there reports of a good season.

Everywhere else cattle and sheep are being fed hay and straw on bare pastures, on which there is less feed than in the blackest winter frost. Even in Cumbria, where there has so far been a magnificent season, re-growth is scarce, and if there is no rain soon, these pastures too will be drying up.

It is this absence of grass which is the most spectacular feature of the drought. Harvest, except in the far North, is complete, and the fields of stubble look much the same as they do in a normal year. But with the absence of any green field, the whole country is desiccated. To make matters worse, large numbers of trees, principally the shallow-rooted ones, are dying in places. Some would say that this is how the deserts started.

The drought is beyond the experience of most of us farming in Britain. I have seen worse conditions in Australia and South America, but there they are to be expected, and the vegetation and the farming systems have been evolved to cope. But this is something new and terrifying, which by some quirk of nature has attacked the most productive areas of England and North Western France, and unaccountably left out Scotland.

It has been a progressive climatic phenomenon. A very dry

winter led to a shortage of about 50 per cent of normal rainfall in many areas. The worst effects of this shortage are being increasingly measured by the failure of wells and the emptying of reservoirs. There was in most districts, however, sufficient moisture in the soil to make for good spring growth of cereals, grass, hay and silage crops.

Until early June most arable crops still looked very well and then came the heat wave which culminated in 10 days or so of temperatures in the 90s at the end of June and the beginning of July. Until then the prospects for the harvest had mostly been excellent, and with normal summer temperatures of around the 70s, grain crops would not have been dehydrated and killed as they were.

It is at about this time that farmers began to feel the first direct effects of the drought. Potatoes and sugar beet on the lighter land began to suffer, and where there is no irrigation the prospects have got steadily worse. Sugar beet has great powers of recovery and many crops could still yield reasonably well, but it is certain that the British Sugar Corporation's early hope of 1m. tonnes of sugar will be missed by a wide margin this year.

Potatoes do not recover so well. Once the crop begins to mature any rain will cause the tubers to grow out, that is to produce extra tubers none of which will make a yield, and the process spoils the original sample. Potato prices are already beginning to take off and are in advance of last year's levels at this time. Only farms with sufficient irrigation look like getting a reasonable yield.

The estimates of the grain harvest now completed verge from the disastrous to the disappointing, but exact figures are hard to establish. Most farmers take a very subjective view of their results and are apt to colour their reports by their mood of the moment. In general terms, however, crops in the south and east are the worst and things improve the further north one travels. But the bulk of the UK grain comes from the south and east in normal years which underlines the seriousness of the situation. Only in Scotland do yields approach the normal.

Amid the general gloom there are happy farmers who by some accident of a chance thunderstorm or farming some very good land, have come off well. But they do not make a significant impact on the final outturn. Few farmers weigh the grain as it comes into their stores and although the bulk may look good the actual weight of the grain is well down this year.

Probably the biggest disappointment has been autumn-sown wheat, of which a record 3m. acres was planted. This usually does very well in a hot dry summer. It looked good too but pessimists said that the extremely hot weather of July would stop the grains swelling to their normal size and thus reduce yield substantially. Farmers have found that yields are some 20 to 25 per cent down on what they would have expected in a normal year from autumn-sown wheat.

An added factor in the reduced wheat yields could have been an attack of aphids during June and July which seems to have affected the whole country. This is only the second year that this has been experienced. Most farmers sprayed the aphids and killed them, but by the time this was finished it is possible that the damage had been done.

If any pattern was discernible, it was that the earliest sown crops did the best, probably because they were able to become well established during the mild winter which allowed growth to continue. This gave them some reserves with which to stand the stress of the summer months.

Autumn-sown barley did relatively well, better perhaps than wheat, probably because it is an early ripening crop, and was already beyond harm when the heat came in July. But this is not widely grown being about 15 per cent of the total barley crop of more than 5m. acres.

Spring barley has verged from the disastrous to the disappointing. It is the main source of malting barley and some is exported for malting to the rest of the EEC. This year samples suitable for malting have been scarce, and maltsters have paid very high prices for what they fancied. The premium for good malting barley is £15 per tonne above that for feed. In more normal times it is often less than £5.

The final result can only be guessed at this time. Last year's outturn was probably between 13.5 and 14m. tonnes, well down on the 1974 figure of nearly 16m. But 1974 was an exceptional harvest, and 14m. tonnes is much nearer the average. If this year's harvest is really as bad as it appears, it could be as low as 12m. tonnes or even less. This is a depressing forecast but I am driven to it by the total absence of optimistic reports of good yields from any part of the country, and by the strength of the trade for the few good samples of malting barley.

The harvest shortfall is already being reflected in the very firm trade for all grains especially those of feed grains. Spot prices for feed barley are up at least £10 per tonne on last year's levels and January futures at £82 per tonne compared with £66 a year ago. The situation is likely to get worse as farmers realise just what the extra winter feeding is going to mean.

In most of the UK livestock farmers reckon they can feed their cattle and sheep on grass from April to November, and then maintain them through the winter on the hay and silage made at the period of maximum growth. Most dairy farmers are now faced with having to feed winter maintenance rations for at least eight months, as they started feeding in early August. But these maintenance rations are in most cases just what they say. Production has to come from supplementary feed of grain and protein. Few farmers budget for much reserve of maintenance over the normal winter requirements, so this means that the dairy farmer for instance will have to purchase feeding stuffs not only for production but for maintenance as well.

In some respects the situation for maintenance feed is better than it was in 1975. There has been a very good hay and silage crop almost everywhere and also the yield and quality of barley straw is much better than last year.

Prices for hay and straw are only now reaching last year's levels. Farmers are still hoping that rains soon could provide some grazing, although most have given up any thought of getting extra crops of silage. But with every day the drought persists the hope of worthwhile grazing for cattle diminishes. Sheep, which graze much more closely than cattle, could well benefit from growth whenever it should restart.

It is customary to sow down grass seeds for next year's grazing under a growing crop of grain, usually barley. Over a very large area of the country these new seeds have died and will have to be resown. This would be perfectly possible in a normal autumn, but the land is now so dry that the seeds may not germinate until it is too late for them to become established before the winter. Most of the more permanent pastures should withstand the drought and start growing again when it is over, but there have been losses which could put next year's spring grazing very much at risk.

This means that dairy farmers' costs for the next winter could be very heavy indeed, and that a number might decide to economise on feed at the expense of optimum milk output. There are signs of this in the fall in milk production being experienced now. This is probably because the majority of herds are autumn calving and farmers have decided it is just as well to dry milking cows off early, rather than spend too much money on trying to maintain milk production which is bound to fall in any case. There has also been a marked increase in cows being culled early for the same reason.

So far there is no sign of any panic among farmers. Prices for most classes of livestock, particularly breeding stock, are still good, but there has been an easing off in prices for younger cattle and sheep. Farmers on the whole think they should be able to stand the effects of a bad season without special help. The most pressing demand that I have heard from individuals is that there should be some method of evening out the tax burden.

August 1976   FINANCIAL TIMES

Christmas

UNLIKE Bing Crosby I have never longed for a white Christmas. As a livestock farmer snow costs me money and the less snow there is through the year the better. It just makes the miseries of farming through an English winter all the worse. Particularly so at Christmas and the New Year which now seems to be telescoped into one long holiday. This means that all work is on an overtime basis and the hindrances caused by snow and frost in burst pipes and frozen troughs and the costs of extra feed because of the lack of grazing are enormously increased.

There is a foolish saying that a green Christmas fills the churchyards; don't you believe it. The greener the Christmases, and fortunately in the South of England they are in the majority, the better my stock and crops and I survive into another spring. Even so the only really good thing to be said about December 25 is that by that day the sun has begun its slow climb back to our latitudes and the days are getting perceptibly longer.

But I have suffered. . . .

Before the war I used to milk my cows in a portable milking shed in the field, called a bail: a system much at risk with snow, and I remember once when snow and Christmas coincided when I was actually milking.

On this particular Christmas afternoon I was relieving a cowman and arrived at the bail about 2 p.m., to find it silent, the cows in a huddle at the other end of the field, a foot of snow and no sign of my mate. I hadn't far to look for him. Tied to the fence of the nearby pub was the horse and cart which carried the churns and feed for the cows. Inside I found Stan topping up his Christmas cheer and in very good form as well.

I joined him for a while, and then persuaded him to come and help me milk. He was very cheerful about it, and by this time so was I. We drove to the bail, chased the cows in to their pen, unthawed the pipeline which was frozen, and started milking. It was a brute of an afternoon, the wind getting colder every minute and snowing hard. But somehow we didn't seem to feel it. In fact we began to feel uncomfortably hot. Whatever the landlord had spliced the beer with, had made us impervious to the cold. We were sweating. I took off my overcoat, then my jacket and before long was down to my shirt sleeves and so was Stan. Then we thought the cows would milk better if we sang to them and so we did. Because we had been late in starting we were singing well as the local churchgoers forced their way through the snow to evensong. But next morning at 5 a.m. things didn't look so good. There had been more snow which we had to dig out, we couldn't get warm, the cows kicked the buckets and stamped on our feet. The Christmas spirit had left them (and us) entirely and what was worse the milk which had been up the afternoon before was down. The only explanation I can think of is that when conditions are atrocious it is better to be tight than sober.

Other Christmases are remembered for various accidents

inseparable from farming life. A herd of cows or sheep gets out and tramples over neighbouring gardens. Angry people interrupt my Christmas dinner with complaints, not realising that the joys of living in the country must be paid for. Only last year I took a last look around my pigs just before going in to lunch, only to find that two enormous boars had had a fight, and one had broken its leg. It took one-and-a-half hours to get a slaughterman to come and put him out of his misery and haul him away. Disasters invariably start on holidays.

In the 1930s farm workers only enjoyed Christmas if they were lucky as a privilege and not as a right. They certainly had no holiday on Boxing Day. Farmers of course could take a break and one of the customs in Wiltshire, although I never saw it actually performed, was to go out and shoot 12 blackbirds before Christmas lunch. What the origin of this particular slaughter was I never discovered (four and 20 blackbirds baked in a pie?). And I never indulged in the sport myself. But as game shooting is forbidden on Christmas Day, the addict could keep his eye in before the customary tenant shoot on Boxing Day.

Boxing Day shoots, coming as they do towards the end of the shooting season, were often a free-for-all. Almost anyone used to be invited, and no one took it with the deadly serious- ness that unfortunately characterises so many farmers' shoots today. Almost everyone came out replete with food and drink and could be relied upon to miss a number of birds so as to safeguard the next year's stock.

One Boxing Day I shot a pheasant the last drive, then caught a plane to Australia where three days later, before the days of jets, my friends had delayed their Christmas dinner, turkey and plum pudding until my arrival. The thermometer topped the century and the beer flowed like Niagara until New Year's Eve when my host suddenly bundled me into a car to drive some hundreds of miles into the interior to shoot kangaroos. On New Year's Day I shot one—not quite a right and left.

I HAVE had half a dozen Christmases and New Years abroad, particularly in the southern hemisphere, where instead of snow and ice, drought, great heat or torrential rain has been the rule.

I had landed in the Argentine with a load of sheep from New Zealand and promptly began to look for work. I found that all jobs except for the lowliest, had Spanish as a first essential. I spoke no Spanish, so I got a labouring job on a big *estancia* south of Buenos Aires where, after a couple of months, I hoped to learn enough Spanish to rise in the social scale. It was hard monotonous work, and the food, boiled beef at midday, and roast beef at night, with very little else was monotonous. However, on Christmas Day we were given a treat: *'asado con cuero'*, calf in its skin. A big calf was killed and skewered on fencing stakes with the skin still on, facing an open fire. There it cooked for two or three hours. This system makes sure that all the juices remain in the meat. The minute it was judged properly cooked we were invited to try it. No plates were used. The procedure was to cut a strip of skin and meat from the carcase, then slice a suitable mouthful almost to the last shred, which held it on until you got it between your teeth. Then a slick upper cut with the knife which everyone carried taking care not to take off the tip of your nose, and the morsel was in your mouth.

It was absolutely delicious, particularly on that first occasion that I tasted it. To avoid burning our hands we used two small pieces of hard bread—*galleta*—which used to be delivered to the *estancia* every two months. With difficulty they could be swallowed when soaked in gravy. For drink we had wine, *cana*, a sort of brandy, finishing up with *mate*, a holly-leaf tea, which kept scurvy at bay. I can't remember when I enjoyed a meal so much or felt so full afterwards.

When it was over I thought I would like a swim. The owners of the *estancia* had a swimming pool. This was reserved for them and not for the workers. While the family were enjoying their sophisticated meal indoors I crept through the grounds, took off my clothes, and swam a few lengths in the nice warm milky water until I suddenly remembered the awful stories I had heard of cramp affecting those who swam after a heavy meal.

I remember a more recent Christmas or rather New Year in Colombia, where the New Year is often more highly thought of. I had travelled from Bogota in the highlands to the jungles near the Magdelena river with Antonio, a politician looking for a seat in Parliament who was going to give some sort of a bribe in the shape of a new bridge to a village in his prospective constituency. At least I think it was a bribe.

We spent the night on a nearby ranch and reached the village about 10 o'clock. The cheque for the local bridge was handed over with due ceremony, and then we adjourned to a pub with a long verandah where Antonio, myself, our wives and some children and 40 or 50 villagers sat down in the shade of the tin roof, and began on the beer.

The Colombian barmaids understand the principles of serving drink excellently. As soon as the top was off one of our bottles, another was put in its place, and although Colombian beer is not particularly strong, the effect of sheer quantity is pleasing in a hot climate. If by any chance the conversation flagged a bottle of spirits was produced and passed around to top up with. During the course of the morning I heard some conversation going on about a *gallina*, which means hen. A few minutes later there was a violent squawking in the distance and we were told that chicken would be served when it was cooked.

At about 4 p.m. the hen was pronounced cooked, banana leaves were laid on the table, the cooking pots emptied on to them and we helped ourselves. Only the gravy was digestible.

All through the long afternoon we drank beer and made political speeches; about 50 people spoke on various political questions and they then looked expectantly at me. What could I do but uphold the honour of Britain and the Financial Times. I embarked on a rousing endorsement of my friend Antonio and all he stood for. My Spanish, although fluent, could not have been very good. Antonio did not then and has not since secured his rightful place in his country's parliament.

And for this Christmas I am doing something completely different. No travel, no excitement. I am leaving the farm in good hands and burying myself in one of the furthest extremities of the British mainland where nothing happens and telephones never ring. Rather like a beautiful but I hope temporary grave.

December 1978   FINANCIAL TIMES

JOC was always suspicious of 'the trade', and when he was invited to write a series of articles for Agritrade *in 1978, he duly obliged.*

The Supply Industry

MANY years ago I purchased a farm and as completion date approached I found that my expectations of cash flow were rather too optimistic. This meant that there would be a yawning gap between my overdraft limit and the sum required, something like £3/4000.

Not wishing to approach the Bank Manager again, I asked the head of a firm of agricultural merchants, with whom I used to deal, to see if by providing my seed, corn and fertiliser on tick, they would bridge the gap. This they agreed to do—the transaction was satisfactorily completed and in due course the merchants got their money.

They also earned a concrete expression of my gratitude in that, as long as their quotations were not outrageously high, they got my business for quite a number of years afterwards. Whether this gratitude on my part actually cost me money I couldn't say. But it does illustrate a point which often used to be claimed by agricultural merchants—that when times were hard they supported the farmers very materially.

Now, I feel that I have paid my debt to the merchanting industry and that I am free to consider them with complete impartiality.

In the old days, the head of each merchant house was an individual, trading on his own—with his own money—dealing in the main with similarly independent farmers. Everybody knows just how arbitrary and bloody minded independent businessmen can be!

The conflict between them—and I always think of trade as

a sort of conflict of wits—can be interesting and exciting. But alas those days are passing.

Today we seem to be dealing either with branches of one or other of the great groups or with the remnants of the country merchants who, it seems to me, are becoming almost as bureaucratic as their big business allies.

I do not hanker for the old days and here is just one example.

Not more than 25 years ago, a merchant in the West of England rang me up out of the blue and asked if I had any barley to sell. After a certain amount of argument I sold him 100 tons a month for the next six months at a price I then considered satisfactory and asked him about references. *'Don't worry about that'*, there would be a cheque in the post tomorrow. So indeed there was, for four months supply.

For several years after this, the head of this firm came to lunch in October,—we had a deal, a deposit was paid and everything went beautifully. Then, the worst happened. The firm was sold to a major group, and immediately things fell apart.

Different drivers were employed, who didn't know how to switch on the augers if no one was about; there were quibbles about dust in the grain, but more important, payment was not made until the third week of the month following delivery.

So you see, my experiences with the change-over from the family merchant to the big firm have not been too happy.

You may say that my attitude is out of touch with the times. That big business is inescapable in modern life and these huge conglomerations, with their vast resources, are essential in the modern world.

I just don't believe it.

As soon as the individual trader begins to employ staff, his overheads mount and mount. Professor Parkinson described it all very well in his treatise and it applies to every single human enterprise. My experience has always been that when dealing with a trader, or almost sole trader, you get instant attention at any time of the day or night and any day of the week. But try ringing a medium sized enterprise even a minute or two before 9 a.m. or just after 5.30 p.m. and the best you will do is get an 'ansafone'.

I make a policy of never doing business with the firm which would like to take my order on an 'ansafone' during what I would conclude to be normal business hours, say from 7 a.m.–7 p.m.—which are the hours I work myself.

I normally direct all my business to the private firms because, generally speaking, their quotations are lower. Even if they are not, they usually are a lot sharper in replying than the major chains—if one should call them chains, as indeed they are, chains on progress.

If I send out a quotation for fertilisers or seeds or anything else, I expect to get a reply by 'phone, or at least by letter, within 24 or 36 hours.

The spread of replies is quite extraordinary. Some taking at least a week to arrive, even if made in the first instance by telephone. The slowest answers usually are from the biggest firms. Don't ask me why, it is just a matter of fact and a fact which should be giving their boards of directors considerable concern.

Like most farmers of my generation, I am a bad co-operator, preferring to paddle my own canoe as far as is possible. I have never found that individual co-operatives—and I belong to a couple—necessarily give me a better deal than I can get elsewhere. By the same token, I don't bother with a grain group to pool my returns over the year with a lot of others.

But the tendency towards what might be called the rationalisation of merchanting into the big groups is bound to bring about a corresponding reaction from farmers of the younger generation.

The margin between what the farmer gets for his produce and what the consumer pays, appears to be gradually increasing.

Whether justly or not, merchants are believed to be creaming some of this margin into their own pockets. Undoubtedly, they couldn't afford their premises or staffs if they didn't.

In the same way, in the supply of materials to farms, some of the overheads appear to be excessive to our simple minds.

Why don't we form the co-operatives which would presumably narrow that margin a little?

I think the reason is that until just recently farming has been too profitable in Britain to bring about this development, although the Milk Marketing Board shows what can be done in this line.

But in the future, it is quite likely that the margins will not be so generous, and pressure will arise from farmers to institute control, as much as they can, of their produce, a bit further along the chain to the miller, to the maltster, the butcher and so forth.

I am not saying such development will necessarily improve farmers' incomes, but it will probably make them feel better just the same.

In any case, the rest of the countries in the Common Market are tremendous co-operators, and governments of most of the countries have implemented statutes which give co-operatives enormous advantages as compared with individual traders. There are cheap loans, restrictions on commercial firms and so on.

It won't be long before, as an alternative to abusing Ministers of Agriculture—as British farmers are so prone to do,—they direct their attention to co-operative trading.

A direction in which any harassed minister would be happy to see them go.

T HE only agrochemical that I can remember being in common use in my youth was Bluestone or Copper Sulphate. It was used indiscriminately to cure foot rot in sheep or dress seed corn against smut.

Progressive farmers varied the foot rot treatment with Stockholm tar. Then some brave men experimented with sulphuric acid for killing charlock—which sometimes increased the crop yield by keeping the weed at bay, but also occasionally killed the barley. It was also hostile to lovers. An English lady who had emigrated to Australia asked me if farmers still made their fields dangerous to those indulging in a tumble in what she obviously took to be long grass.

Then, Dr Blackman of Oxford performed some of the first experiments with hormone weedkillers on my farm. He had some yellow substance the name of which escapes me. It covered the crops and the rabbits with a yellow tinge and it had dangerous side effects.

I was talking to the good Doctor one day, when without a word, he leapt into his car and drove straight across the crop to where one of his students was working, sounding the horn all the time. When I eventually caught up with him he explained that if the student had gone on pounding the mixture to soften it, there would have been an explosion which would not only have interrupted the course of science, but the student's life as well.

Since those days, the farming scene has been invaded by a plethora of chemicals, which are claimed to be able to kill almost every weed and pest if only we, the farmers, will use them. This has been far from being an unmixed blessing.

Everyone must pay tribute to the first of the hormones which did away with charlock. But did our fields become free of weeds in consequence? We lost the charlock it is true. But it was replaced on my own farm by runch or white charlock and cleavers with which we had never had any problem before.

These weeds had undoubtedly been present in minute quantities, but their expansion had been held in check by the charlock. They were easy enough to kill with a new and slightly more expensive spray. And no sooner had the last two been conquered than other annual and biannual weeds appeared, each needing still more expensive and sophisticated chemicals to deal with them.

In consequence, when paying my increasing bills for chemicals, I wonder if research has not been taking the wrong direction. That instead of allowing chemists to find new products to overcome specific situations and weeds, botanists could not be engaged to investigate the possibility of setting one weed off against the other in order to establish by natural means a reasonable environment in which the crop could grow.

Economists could then be engaged to work out the level of weed infestation which a crop could stand without losing out financially on an expensively sprayed crop.

It is a point which must be of concern to manufacturers as well. The farmers' purse is not bottomless, so cost effectiveness should be the No. 1 priority in the minds of the salesmen who seem to be attacking my farm in increasing numbers.

But they are not really salesmen. They are now called advisers, employed by the chemical companies to confuse my poor mind with the science that my lack of education has denied me. Once the adviser has softened up the victim, the salesman who accompanies him takes the order.

I am not in any way attacking the ethics of those in this trade. Everyone, I am always being told, be they merchants, manufacturers, their advisers and the salesmen, has to live. All I am concerned with is that they should not make too good a living out of me.

I must confess that there was a time when I was an absolute sucker for the chemical aids to farming. My land is hard and flinty, and I sought everything that would ease the dreadful wear on metal, rubber and fuel that conventional cultivations entailed. I could say that I was one of the pioneers of minimal cultivations, or even of none at all. The results were disappointing, certainly not up to the claims of those who manufactured the products.

I have found, in the end, that there is nothing to beat sound traditional cultivations as a basis of arable farming, I am not dogmatic about this, I still use chemicals where I think they may have an application, I still minimise my cultivations where I can. But I have not yet sold my heavy equipment and I don't think I will for a while yet.

I am also very concerned that similar substances are sold under different brand names and very often at different prices to do the same job. Before the war the Ministry of Agriculture used to publish a list of synonyms for seed corn in order to counter the activities of certain seedsmen who used to use different names for common varieties of grain.

There is, I am aware, an official guide to chemicals, *Approved Products for Farmers and Growers*, but it is not an easy one to follow, and does not in my opinion give sufficient advice on the relative values of the different formulations.

I spend quite a long time working out the best buys every year, and sometimes this does not please the sales representatives who call or ring me up. They may not be agents for my particular choice—this is another area where disinterested advice from the merchant may give way to commercial interest.

I am re-emphasising the cost factor because it is, I think, paramount and if disregarded could result eventually in sales resistance. I have been very struck when visiting the grain growing areas on the Continent—Schleswig-Holstein, Belgium and Northern France—by the very high levels of chemical application to the grain crops. But on analysis two things struck me forcibly.

The first was that chemical use followed high grain prices, prices that in many cases were and still are substantially above those ruling in the UK.

This gave farmers a margin in which to gamble on increasing yields by spending money on chemicals. The tramline systems which have been developed in all these areas were a direct consequence of this. I have nothing against tramlining as an aid to accurate spraying and manuring, but it can also facilitate the spending of a lot of unnecessary money.

This leads me to the next point about the Europeans. I did not think that in the end, their yields, considering the quality of their land, were any better than those on similar land in Britain grown under much similar systems.

Therefore it seemed to me that they had paid out a fair bit of money and complicated their systems to an extent unjustified by the actual weight of crop harvested. But the real cost of this had been concealed by the high prices they had been receiving.

In spite of the foregoing I must acknowledge the assistance that the chemists have rendered to farming over the last 30 years. The burden of my argument is that we would all in the end profit if we were more selective in our use of their products.

ON rereading the articles I have been writing in this series it could be said that they have mainly been a diatribe at the whole of the supply industry. If I were one of the victims—if I could call my readers that—I would say they were pretty unconstructive. So perhaps I had better try and remedy the situation as far as I can.

The farmer's ideal merchant is one who will supply him with his requisites at the cheapest possible prices, and at the same time sell his produce to the ultimate user with as low a margin as possible.

My aim has always been to cut out the middleman, the merchant, in both directions. I see no reason, for instance, why I, and a number of my neighbours, should not combine to go to a fertiliser manufacturer and buy our requirements at trade prices. We can pay just as well as any merchant, and there is no logical reason for the merchant, as opposed to the manufacturer, to remain in business.

In the same way, when selling, there is no reason why I should not sell, as far up the chain as I can, to a miller, maltster and compounder. After all, if deliveries fail I have to stand the racket, even if I have sold to a merchant.

It could be said that this attitude is not only selfish, but short-sighted. It means that the merchant's expertise is not being used to the best advantage. It is surely up to the merchants to prove otherwise.

I believe for their own sakes farmers should be prepared to do as much as possible of their own business, either alone or collectively. Otherwise they risk eventually being confined to their farms and their farming, with a considerable loss of independence and actual cash.

This has actually happened over the years in Australia and New Zealand. There, farmers were so much in the thrall of the big pastoral companies, that they seemed to have no opportunity for advancing the real business of their industry themselves. These overseas farmers had literally no side of their business beyond the farm gate which they could call their very own, for many years.

So I would not want to see any further extension of such present operations as the pig and poultry breeding and fattening schemes where the farmer is in many cases little more than an employee of the merchant or compounder, although he does not have the benefit of National Insurance or a union to sustain him.

I lay no blame on the present conduct of these schemes, which have their attractions to those lacking capital. But I think the margins in these types of production are becoming so tight that there is no room for another party to become involved.

This is a point which has I think been lost sight of recently. The fact is that membership of the Common Market will eventually push the cost of animal feeds to unprecedented levels. This will eventually bring about a situation here, which has already arrived on the Continent, where pig and poultry production is basically in the hands of the family farmer, who doesn't count his labour cost.

I don't know whether this is such a bad thing. One of the problems with British farming, as against that in Europe, is that units have become so large and farmers so few, that farmers have no political power at all. It is almost certain that the current effects of capital taxation, and the reduction in margins, will make for generally smaller holdings and perhaps even an increase in the numbers engaged. The trend to much larger holdings was due to the accident of death duties and the slump coinciding in the 1920s and 30s. The situation may well reverse itself.

This you might say could well be to the advantage of the merchant and trader. Small farmers are never likely to go in for the independent business attitudes that the larger ones do now. This is true. But small farmers are much more likely to form and stick to the co-operative principle than large ones.

So far, co-operation among farmers in Britain has been little more than a joke. Farmers are for it in principle, as long as they don't have to practise it themselves. But small farmers cannot afford to be so disdainful. If you study the beginnings of co-operation in Denmark, France and elsewhere you will find that it all arose from the determination of farmers to unite to fight the exploitation, real or imagined, of the purchasers of their products.

Being large in numbers, they were able to compel governments to listen to them and give co-operatives advantages denied to individual or private traders. If you really want to hear a moan, listen to a French merchant talking about the aid granted to the wealthy co-operative just down the road.

If you don't believe that the day of a return to smaller units is on the way, just think of paying £100 a week for labour, EEC prices for feed and getting non-guaranteed prices for pigs and poultry and with the milk market under very considerable threat. I think the change in enterprise size is bound to come, and it is wise to keep abreast of the change, because small farmers here will follow the same trend as on the Continent.

This means of course that the present co-operative movement here will have to pull its socks up. At present, most co-ops are simply another merchant organisation.

Success in future trading will no doubt go to the organisations which can streamline their costs and capital use to the minimum. The co-operative principle, I have always thought, should be to maximise farmers' returns, while minimising the cost of inputs. At present we are all too prosperous to worry about the odd few pence per tonne. But this might all change.

I say this in all seriousness. If, as I have, you study farming history anywhere in the world, it is far from being a constant story of progress, profitability, loss or anything else. It is inherently cyclical and unstable.

At the moment we in Britain are going through a period of almost unparalleled farming prosperity compared to many other parts of national life. It is almost certain that the circumstances that bring about this happy situation will alter, and the whole of the industry might well change in structure and attitudes. These changes could be summarised as follows:

- A reduction in the scale of enterprise on livestock holdings beginning with pigs, poultry and probably followed by dairying, leading to more family farming.
- Consequent increasing governmental care of the co-operatives.
- A decline in the arable areas intensively farmed. This, because climatically and geologically Britain, except for a small area, is inferior to much of the rest of the Continent. If you doubt me look at the fact that yields of both sugar beet and potatoes and grain are inferior, and the sugar quota is under threat.

These views are unfashionable and could be wrong, but they should not be left out of account in any long term planning by the supply industry.

March, April and August 1978   AGRITRADE

Rex Paterson

I KNEW Rex Paterson for well over forty years. When I met him first he was farming at New Zealand Farm, Chute in Wiltshire, and just beginning the expansion which was to make him the largest dairy farmer in Britain. In those days things were rough. There was no time for more than working, eating and sleeping. He and his wife milked a batch of sixty cows bought on credit, in a bail on hire purchase, and on a farm which the vendor, a cattle dealer, had found it impossible to resell.

His persistence and parsimony paid off. By 1935 he was milking 3 bails and ready to leave the Chute Hills for the lusher lands of Sussex and Hampshire. He never really looked back. From then on his progression was like that of many others who grew up from the Depression, except that he concentrated singlemindedly on cows.

From the earliest years of our friendship I had been impressed by the quality of his mind. At Chute long before there were the means to implement it he had plans for the buckrake which really came to fruition only when Ferguson produced the hydraulic lift. The earlier models had been fitted to ex-army gun tractors among other things. His other inventions—the Fertispread is the best known—were all designed to perform in the most economical manner possible the essential jobs of a simple farming system.

Basically Paterson's farming aim was to produce milk from grass and grass alone on the New Zealand model. To this end he dotted his Hampshire farms with 80 to 100 cow units on land on which for much of the post-war period large scale arable farming might well have been more profitable. His men were not supposed to feed any more than the minimum of compound or grain. Each bail's performance was carefully monitored on a most exhaustive recording system which showed just how much more efficient one man was than another. Yet for all the thoroughness of the records they did not lead to the good men being fostered and the sluggards being sacked. It seemed that the whole recording system was of academic interest only.

I used to point this out to him, and also the fact that while he was making an undoubted success of his system of all-grass farming, others were being equally successful in keeping cows on concentrates and hay. He would argue long and patiently that his system was right, and this belief became an obsession in later life. His methods, founded in the Depression, were becoming out of place, certainly until the next Depression comes along.

Nevertheless for more than thirty years his thinking about grass and grass farming had an enormous impact, and the fact that he made people think about it, even if they subsequently disagreed with him, was a tribute. I never thought his overall concept was wrong: simply that he would allow no room for compromise.

But he had one quality to be valued above all others: a most wealthy man by any standards, he was always the same interested man of simple tastes whom I had first met milking his own cows on the Chute hills. Success never really spoiled Rex Paterson.

• • •

January 1979 BRITISH FARMER AND STOCKBREEDER

Sir Henry Plumb

THE forthcoming departure of Sir Henry Plumb from the presidency of the National Farmers' Union marks a fundamental break in the Union's policies which have endured since the war.

The close links which were formed between the Union and the Ministry in the interests of wartime food production were carried on by Lord Netherthorpe, the Union's first executive president, and his successors, until Common Market entry was achieved in 1972.

The basis of this association was the Agriculture Act of 1947 which laid down that the Government would provide the support for 'that part' of the nation's food it was deemed necessary and desirable to grow at home.

As world supplies and imports increased from the mid-1950s the discussions about 'that part' became more and more acrimonious. The Government of the day, notably in the 1960s when Sir Christopher Soames was Minister, enforced an end to the open-ended guarantees by imposing limits on supported production with what were called standard quantities.

In the immediate post-war years, Lord Netherthorpe, in

many respects the most able negotiator it has been my privilege to see in action, appeared to feel obliged to use his considerable prestige with farmers to moderate their more irrational claims in the national interest, particularly when food was still short.

His successor, Lord Woolley, was faced with Sir Christopher Soames at his fiercest. He could do little but mitigate what farmers regarded as the Government's hostility.

Sir Gwilym Williams had a fairly rough ride too, because for a start at least the 1964 Labour Government carried on the Soames policy.

But when Sir Henry took office in 1971 the climate changed. Mr Heath's Government was determined to join Europe and prices were allowed to escape from the strait-jacket of standard quantities to some extent in a series of good annual price reviews. Since membership of the EEC was achieved there has been a steady increase in returns, enough to give Sir Henry a fairly easy time.

There have been rebellions among the membership, notably in 1974 when farmers tried to barricade the ports against Irish imports. But this was all handled well and the protests subsided as they normally do when prices rise again.

Meanwhile Sir Henry embraced Europe with an enthusiasm worthy of several better causes. He became president of COPA, the European farmers' lobby for two years (he has a weakness for presidencies). He appeared to settle down well with his fellow farm leaders in Europe. But it never seemed he really understood the conflicts of interest that make up the membership of COPA.

Once the Labour Government of 1974 came in, Sir Henry found in Fred Peart, the new Minister, a person after his own heart. Like many converts Mr Peart, now elevated to Lord Peart, took his new found *communautaire* beliefs so seriously as to prejudice his powers of reason. It seems extraordinary that one who had been in politics for 30 years was so trustful of the disinterest of his fellow ministers in Brussels.

During this time Sir Henry cemented firmly an even closer relationship with the Minister. So much so that it became obvious to the Government that what it thought were national interests in the way of food prices, were to be eroded by more and more concessions on the Green Pound and other matters.

Candidly Yours . . .

Fred Peart departed to the Lords and Sir Henry faced a very different ball game. In John Silkin, a pronounced anti-Marketeer, he found a Minister who knew little of farming but who carried out his Government's orders and who, at first anyway, had little concern about the long, close relationship between the Ministry and the NFU.

Mr Silkin is always polite. But he does not mind farmers' hostility, nor that of his fellow Ministers in Brussels, who in any case almost always put the interests of their own countries first, just as he does.

At this time another change was coming. Mr Silkin realised that farming policy was no longer being made in Whitehall but in Brussels. During the 1976 pig crisis he instituted a special subsidy which ran for about four months until it was terminated on orders from the Commission.

This I believe was the first blow to Sir Henry's confidence. The whole relationship built up between the NFU and the Ministry had been shattered. Even if the two agreed about something they would have to be subject to the agreement of Brussels.

Here the union has no real pull, its only support among a welter of opposing interests in the Community headquarters is the Minister himself pursuing a much wider overall brief.

There was another blow. Some months ago, Mr Asher Winegarten, for many years the union's chief economic and political strategist, became seriously ill and he is still not back at work. In April George Cattell, the new director-general, left to take over FMC. Bereft of these solid advisers, Sir Henry has undoubtedly come to understand the need for getting fresh minds to work and has stood down.

He is only aged 53. He has a farm to which it will not be easy to return, and he has set his sights on the European Parliament of which there could be many worse members.

He is popular with farmers, although some are beginning to question his blind advocacy of the Community. He does deserve another job where his talents could be employed. Farmers are not notably generous to their retired politicians, but Sir Henry Plumb deserves well of them.

November 1978   FINANCIAL TIMES

The Incomplete Angler

I HAVE fallen between two fishing stools, if you see what I mean.

It's all to do with the British class system. As a child of industrious parents, and educated by the excessively puritan doctrines of saving and self-denial, all my early fishing had to be free. It would have been almost incredibly spendthrift to have invested in fishing holidays where game fish, trout and salmon were available. This was reserved for the very rich who were born to it, or the profiteers who had grabbed enough money to be able to buy such fishing for themselves.

So like the great mass of the British people I had to start with coarse fishing, in competition with many more expert than I. That is not to say I never caught a trout during my youth; but I cannot be said to have been a purist.

Some miles from my home at the time was a chalk stream, the Gade. Some quite nice trout were to be seen under the bridge which takes the main road across some old hatches. It wasn't difficult to cycle up to the parapet and rest against it admiring the view—while at the same time dangling a hand line into the water.

There was no finesse, it was just a question of dropping the worm into the slack. I always used a worm, hauling in fast when it was taken, stuffing the victim into my satchel and shooting off at top speed. I was never caught. But one of my acquaintances, determined to do the job in style, set up a proper fly rod and arrived at the bank at sunrise—only to meet the keeper and have his tackle confiscated.

Once home, I was able to convince my mother, who at the time did not know any better, that my trout came from the canal, my only legal fishing venue.

I must have been about eight when I caught my first fish. I was in the charge of a French governess on a Gloucestershire farm and she had heard that there were eels in the farm pond.

She made me up a rod and line complete with bent pin for a hook and baited with a worm from the garden. I dropped it in the water and it was immediately taken. I was petrified. '*Tire vite'*, she shouted in my ear. I jerked the rod and a wriggling eel shot out of the water and over my shoulder, to be grabbed and put in the governess's bag. I caught about half a dozen before they stopped biting and I gave up for the day.

The next morning she showed them to me swimming headless in the saucepan in which they were to be boiled. I burst into tears, taking no notice of her assurance that the wriggles were only produced by nerves. I have never willingly caught an eel since, and will only eat them smoked to this day.

There then followed several years of coarse fishing, though by then I was well equipped with rod, line and a bucket for the fish I was going to catch. I spent the best part of two years by the Hampstead ponds, shoulder-to-shoulder with many other fishermen watching floats that never bobbed. I can't remember ever catching anything, not even a gudgeon. But I did have a hand in catching a hefty carp.

It was the habit of those Hampstead fishermen to leave their rods supported by forked sticks while they busied themselves throwing in ground bait, drinking beer, eating sandwiches, reading the paper or just sleeping.

Suddenly, there was a commotion just down the line. A rod was plucked violently from its rest and towed round the pond a number of times. Eventually it passed quite close to me, and as I had the longest rod on the day, I lent it to the fisherman

to catch the floating rod. This he did, and eventually brought in the carp, an eight-pounder.

Strangely enough, I had much the same experience last year in Scotland. I was salmon fishing, and on the fifth day of an absolutely blank week I put my rod down with the fly in the water and turned my back to spend a penny. While so occupied, I heard the reel begin to turn. But before I could grab it, the rod had been pulled into the centre of the pool where it sank at once, not to be retrieved until the next morning after the fish had got off.

The moral of this is that when static lining for salmon, or anything else, it is best to secure the butt of the rod. Static lining is unethical, I am told.

I also took up sea fishing on family holidays in Brittany. The cook at our boarding house encouraged me, and like all perfect women was pleased to clean my catch. She also taught me that limpets eaten fresh off the rocks were just as nice as oysters. '*Les huitres des pauvres*,' she would call them.

Sea fishing came to an end during my engagement. In those days fathers-in-law took a keen interest in their daughters' future husbands, and mine gave me a test by taking me on a family cruise on his yacht. I did not do very well. I pulled the wrong ropes, steered in the wrong direction and then, in spite of the fact that I had sailed unscathed around Cape Horn, was sick.

To recover my position, I put a line over the side and soon started to pull in mackerel, which I passed to my intended for her to prepare for the pan. Those who catch the fish, said father, must clean them, and in any case they stink the boat out. I have been a family fish cleaner ever since.

I began to attack the trout in a big way in New Zealand. At one place I worked there was a small stream containing a few small trout. When we killed a sheep it was hung over the water and the blood and other bits used to fall in. The trout, naturally, were nice and plump and would take a chunk of meat on a hook. They had a marvellous flavour, and made a change from mutton at every meal.

There were other means: in the bigger rivers there were some very good fish, and the technique was to fire a .303 bullet into their midst. The shock would stun them and they could be raked in as they floated downstream. It was also possible, although I was never successful, to mix acetelyne and water in a lemonade bottle—one of those with a marble in the neck—and sink it in a pool. Pressure of the gas would make it explode, and up the fish were supposed to float.

This, according to the experts, was nothing like as effective as a Mills grenade. But grenades were scarce in New Zealand at that time. I would never really use such means, of course, but once, while in the Home Guard, I was sorely tempted.

The reason for this uncharacteristic probity was simply that I was becoming increasingly infected with the sporting ethic which, like the work ethic, is one of the most pernicious afflictions to be suffered by mankind.

There are rules in all game fisheries as to the types of baits to be used. The permitted baits are not necessarily those which fish will take as a first or second choice. If they were, rivers and reservoirs would soon become empty, unless fished by coarse fishermen, who put them back and in consequence can use anything.

Living near the River Test, I had heard and even read about the delights of fly fishing, and soon after the war I began to attack the trout legally at last. My slowly increasing economic status had eroded, as it so often does, my penurious principles.

I began by attacking the rivers and lakes of western Ireland with indifferent success. There was always a ghillie in the boat and, while an interesting character of great charm, it was he who always hooked all the fish. I began to lose interest in lake fishing and decided to have a go at dry fly in the Kennet and finally the Test.

A lot of nonsense is talked about dry fly fishing, but the principle is quite simple. All you have to do is to deposit a floating fly within reach of a rising fish without scaring it, in the hopes that it will be taken. The fly should bear some resemblance to those floating down the surface at the time. What skill there is depends on the gentleness with which the fly hits the water.

While still learning, I entered the casting competition at one of the early game fairs. Here the object was to drop the fly in hoops floating on a pool. I noticed my fellow competitors were casting as if there were wary fish around, so that the strong wind was spoiling their accuracy. . . .

I used brute force, splashing the fly in every hoop and walking off with the first prize. My casting was the object of derision and the applause at the prize-giving negligible. I have never won it since, but I regard the subsequent imitation of my technique as the sincerest form of flattery.

The Test, where I have fished for 20 years, has provided the finest antidote to the trials and tribulations of life. When I say to my staff or my family that I am off to the bank, they don't know whether I am going to draw the wages or waste another afternoon.

But it's not always a waste of time. Many years ago I was driven by a thunderstorm to shelter in a fellow rod's Jaguar. All through a long very wet afternoon we talked and supped a little gin. In the end, he disclosed he was the (now retired) editor of this paper. I admitted to being a desultory writer. As a direct consequence I joined the FT.

I wonder who caught whom that day.

April 1979 FINANCIAL TIMES

The Nineteen Eighties

As the '80s came in, so did the downturn in farming prosperity. JOC continued to hand out unpalatable truths and take the ill-educated to task.

Hard Times? Not So!

ANYONE listening to the debates at the NFU annual general meeting could be excused for thinking that the end of farming in this country was just around the corner. Never have I heard such a load of unsubstantiated misery. If, as Richard Butler says, farmers are facing such a bleak future, why are land prices still on the £2,000 an acre mark? Why are there no farms to rent? Why are hordes of young men going to colleges and trying to get into farming by hook or by crook? Why haven't livestock prices crashed?

As for the figures of bank indebtedness, it is said by the banks that much of this demand comes from farmers wanting to buy land. Even so, in terms of asset value I doubt if British farming over all is more than 10 per cent in the red. Compare that with from 50 to 70 per cent in New Zealand, and up to 90 per cent in Denmark. No wonder an increasingly irritated Peter Walker snaps back about marketing improvement and exporting to Europe, as the only bone he has left to throw to an ungrateful dog.

These questions are those put to me by an increasing number of observers from outside industry. They don't see many signs of misery and destitution when they look over the hedge, or have to jump into the gutter to avoid being run down by some farmer's Range Rover or Volvo.

I am well aware that the White Paper showed a net reduction in income ov er the year of 17 per cent for 1979 in real terms. But the sample farm results, which are based on actual farm accounts, showed a rise of 33 per cent. I never understood the gross income calculation which I always thought was purely hypothetical, but the sample farm results are founded on fact.

You could say that the sample farms are selected, and no doubt those who produce the accounts are in the upper end of the farming spectrum. But they exist, and Ministers can read them as well as anyone else. So too can those who make the prices at Brussels. It may be a tactical mistake to let others see success. Good poker players never show their hands. But the convention of letting accounts be published was ingrained years ago in the 1947 Agriculture Act. And conventions, once established, are almost impossible to alter.

One problem with the White Paper is that it is irrelevant to Community membership. The Common Agricultural Policy is supposed to turn the whole of rural Europe into one farm, and there is no logic in a demand for special treatment for one region or one country. I know all member countries are cheating with various forms of national measures. But the fact must be faced that if the CAP is not to be destroyed, it will have to be accepted.

But acceptance appears to be the last thing the delegates to the AGM had in mind. Resolution after resolution asked the British Government to do something or other special for British farmers. One even asked that the threshold price for maize should be reduced. Did not the Cheshire Branch, from which it came, ever read the large print of the CAP rules? These state unequivocally that cereal prices are to be maintained by means of import levies and intervention buying.

I can remember pointing out for years that this facet of the CAP would probably hurt livestock farmers very badly indeed, especially as there would be no real protection for pigs and poultry. My complaints and criticism of the CAP and the Common Market generally were dismissed as of little account.

Fired by their undoubted idealism, the pro-marketeers led by Sir Henry Plumb and others would brook no such basic considerations. Idealists are either dangerous or suckers, and our EEC partners took the chance to follow the old maxim of never giving a sucker an even break.

Anyway we are in now, and the only way to play it is to survive. It is just as well to realise that the Government will do nothing unless it decides to have a real row with the Community, break up the CAP and revert to national policies. It is interesting to note that Mr Walker has now gone on record as saying that surpluses should be the responsibility of national governments. But of course he does not mean the UK Government.

He is more likely thinking of the milk surpluses produced by the Dutch and Irish, proportionately much higher than those of the French and Germans. I must say I agree that in a perfect world they should be cut back to size. But the world is far from perfect, and the fact is that the rest of the Community does not see the problem in the same light at all. There the whole tone is that the overproduction of milk comes from the bigger units.

There is plenty of evidence of this on statistical grounds, i.e. that bigger farms are increasing output more than smaller ones. Hence the demand for a co-responsibility levy based on individual herd output. There is also evidence that some of the increase comes from compound feeding.

This is all very unfair, and a negation of the call for the efficiencies of scale etc. which we have heard so much about for the last ten years or so. It should have been foreseen long ago that British farming was an entirely different ball game.

But the fact must be faced that European competition, as well as being unfair in many respects, e.g. the French lamb import ban and German positive MCAs, is also very real. This is simply because it is largely made up of family farmers employing no labour, and who could sink us in a real economic free-for-all.

If you don't believe me go and spend some time there looking at the real grass roots.

• • •

March 1980   BRITISH FARMER AND STOCKBREEDER

New Zealand on the Rack

THE New Zealand Dairy and Meat Boards are celebrating one hundred years of refrigerated exports to this country. But a guest at one of the parties last week struck a sombre note. How much longer, he asked me, will it be possible to transport dairy produce 12,000 miles across the world, and still show a worthwhile return to the producers.

This is indeed a good question, and one that concerns not only New Zealand farmers but the whole economy of the country. There is a progressive deterioration in the country's external account with the deficit up by 61 per cent to NZ$1,072m. in the year ending February last.

Export receipts, of which farm products provide some 70 per cent have been rising strongly in money terms. But however efficiently farmers work their increasing output is unable to keep ahead of the rising costs of imports and other overseas payments. This is not just a reflection of the current world recession, it was becoming obvious at least a dozen years ago.

In 1970 I got a lot of stick from various New Zealand interests for suggesting, in the FT, that unless the New Zealand Government was prepared to subsidise its farming, the country would be in a bad way. By 1975, in the course of another visit, I heard the then government announce a series of guarantees funded by the exchequer. Since then the Government is guaranteeing the price of meat and wool by supplementing market earnings.

Even with this help, and the progressive devaluation of the New Zealand dollar, down 15 per cent since 1979, farm earnings have not kept pace with costs and there is evidence of a reduction in investment in fertilisers—the basic tool of expansion—this year.

A major problem is the high cost of slaughter and transport between the farm and the wholesale market overseas. For instance, a typical lamb for which the NZ farmer is receiving 31p a lb is selling wholesale in London for 69p. The New Zealand farmer is receiving a government supplement of about 20 per cent in his price.

I have particularly drawn attention to New Zealand because

of all the countries involved in world trade it is probably the most dependent on agricultural exports. But the picture is the same wherever farm exports are a significant proportion of earnings.

Of course New Zealand's situation is made worse by distance from the main markets for temperate products in spite of extraordinary efforts to divert trade away from Britain, which have achieved a measure of success. There are great difficulties elsewhere, particularly in the near East and there are tariff barriers almost everywhere.

Although the dairy product market is showing more resilience, the butter quota to the UK must be in question if the forecasts of the shrinking UK market turn out to be correct. The estimate is that by 1985, butter consumption in Britain will have fallen to 185,000 tonnes, rather less than present UK production.

It is fashionable for primary producing countries to blame the EEC's Common Agricultural Policy for their problem because of high tariffs and lately because of the effects of subsidised exports onto their own traditional markets. In this respect New Zealand is not so badly done by, and there is an arrangement between New Zealand and the Community over dairy products which restricts the wholesale exporting which operates in other sectors.

What really seems to be in question is the ability of a country of 3 million people to maintain its present high standard of living on the output of an agriculture which directly only employs a small proportion of the population. There are few other resources, although some energy will become available in due course, but there is no real industrial base.

The New Zealand authorities recognise this, and have encouraged moves to a more intensified type of farming with some success. Most notable of these has been Kiwi Fruit for which there is a good export demand and there are large expansion schemes. Even so, after five years, exports of horticultural and other non-traditional products amount to only 5 per cent of all agricultural exports.

The New Zealanders are apt to point to the hungry mouths around the world, and rather naively suppose that by some miracle the surplus food will be transmitted to them at prices which will support their production. But where will the money come from?

The real villain of the piece is what the Australian Professor Blaney called the 'Tyranny of Distance'—the high economic cost of transporting high volume, comparatively low value, commodities to markets across the world. This has been aggravated by inflation and high energy costs which show no signs of abating.

It is worth mentioning that in the Falkland Islands today surplus sheep are simply killed as there is no export market. Before refrigeration New Zealand farmers did the same. Refrigeration has supported the country for a century. What miracle will support it for the next?

May 1982   FINANCIAL TIMES

In the '80s, alongside his serious articles, JOC wrote in a much lighter vein for a wider audience.

Snakes in the Grass

I HAVE always been frightened of snakes since I heard in the Argentine how one young landowner met his end. He was walking with his new bride in the estancia orchard when, stretching his hand to a branch to pick her a nectarine, a snake bit him. The roads were impassable to cars and by the time they got him to hospital by horse cart he was dead.

I used at one time rather to fancy myself on a horse. Springing in and out of the saddle in the best Hollywood style. So when some years ago I was helping an Australian farmer to move some sheep I prepared to jump to the ground when a gate wouldn't open from horseback. However while halfway down, as it were, I looked to see what my landing was like and saw an enormous snake. I must have performed the most rapid aborted landing of all time, because seconds later I was back in the saddle and galloping away. 'What the hell's up,' asked Bert, my friend. 'There's a bloody great snake there,' I said. He thought a moment then said 'Pick it up by the tail and crack it.' That I replied 'is something I would sooner watch than try and perform myself, show me the way with the first one.'

So he rode up, studied the snake, and then got off at a safe distance and instead of doing as he suggested picked up an enormous stone and staggered over to the snake with it. The snake by this time, thoroughly alarmed, decided not to wait and slithered off into the rocks. 'What would you have done Bert if I had been bitten,' I asked him. 'That would be easy,' he replied, and from a pouch on his belt he extracted a rusty razor blade and said 'I would slash your leg open with this and then suck the venom out.'

Calling on a friend in the suburb of Perth in Western Australia the other day I was shown a small snake in a jar of spirit. This had stung the family cat, which had only been saved by a visit to the vet at a cost of $30, say £15, and a good deal of fright and excitement all round, during which the youngest child got bitten by a venomous spider, fortunately not a fatal bite, but enough to make the children keep their shoes on in the garden for a week or so.

Another friend, also in Western Australia, reckoned that a cat had saved her own child from a snake. She had left the baby in the garden lying on a rug, and hearing the cat scream, dashed out to find the cat dying in a sort of paralytic agony while the snake was making towards her child. She managed to chase it away, picked up the child, then got a shotgun and killed the snake. Small wonder then when leaving her house I saw a large snake cross the road and ran it over.

I have never actually seen a live adder in this country, though I have seen them dead on the road. But before the war one stretch of downland I rented was infested, and I frequently had sheep bitten by them. These bites were seldom fatal, in fact I can't remember any of them being so, but the sheep used to develop very large swellings particularly around the heads which the snakes had obviously attacked when the sheep were grazing.

However, a neighbour was attending his compost heap, and picking up a handful of material felt a multitude of stings. This was a nest of young adders which he had disturbed and which retaliated in the only way known to them. Taken to hospital he was given the anti-venom and recovered but he had a very nasty illness indeed.

The French call the adder a viper and when staying in France once I went with one of my fellow guests, a Pakistani, for a walk while the orthodox Christians were at Mass. Our way led along the sunny side of a hedge and all of a sudden my companion who was given to long philosophical discourse broke off and started to beat the base of a bush along the track. Presently he stopped and fished out with a stick the battered remains of a viper which was probably sunning itself by the path. 'I'm very conscious of snakes,' he said and so, I might say, am I.

April 1981   FINANCIAL TIMES

April Snows

IN the early morning of the 26th April, a Sunday, my wife woke me with the information that the power was off, and how was she going to cook the lunch and what about the deep freeze? I said we could eat cheese and the deep freeze could be filled with the snow which I saw was blanketing the whole farm. But then I began to think.

I have a great many sheep and two large flocks of these were being confined by electric fences. With no power they were bound to be out. At eight o'clock I set out with a man with a chain saw and we literally cut our way through fallen branches to the first of the flocks.

They were spread over the winter barley and were digging through the snow for an illicit feed. The wires of the fence had become coated with snow and the sheep had probably pushed through them, even before the power was off. Electric fences of two or three wires are much cheaper and more flexible than ordinary ones, but on this particular day I wished I had invested in the more traditional sort.

The next flock was spread over several of my neighbours' farms and after a couple of hours we re-erected the fences, powered them with car batteries and enclosed the sheep.

When I got home the pigman arrived and said that they had no water. Water in this case comes from a supply which relies on an electric pump. So I had to send off and borrow a water tank, which could be filled from a public main. This was also vulnerable because it depends on electricity, but the public reservoir was better stocked than the one I depend on.

The pigman also pointed out that unless we got power back soon, we should be out of feed by the next afternoon because my mill and mixing plant is also electrically driven. The baby pigs depend on infra-red lamps for warmth but luckily they are in well insulated houses.

By this time the water was out in the house, same supply as the pigs, and the cooking was going on with picnic gear, about the only time it is ever used, because I have a thing about carrying gas cylinders in cars. There was, of course, no television but a battery radio informed us of what was going on. We also have the oil lamps with which we furnished our first home many, many years ago. They still work. My wife, who expects the end of the world at any moment, keeps them trimmed.

I tried to ring the Electricity Board every moment I had to spare and got an engaged signal. But I would point out, if any Electricity Board manager reads this, that there would be some comfort to us if we could have some idea as to when a supply would be reconnected.

By mid-day on Monday we got some electricity back, but it was only a single phase and everything works on three phase. Nothing important was working, beyond the television and the deep freeze.

I forgot to add that on the Sunday I was asked to get my snow plough out, but unfortunately the tractor that it fits had been re-equipped with narrow wheels for summer work and it would have been impossible to get it to work for several hours. I did, however, send out a digger and rescued several cars. One of these was taking several people to a distant church. 'Why not worship in Parson Greenfield's church, or even in Parson Whitefield's?' 'We don't want to disappoint Mr Smith', they replied.

For several days we had to feed hay out to the sheep, but we did not lose any. The lambs were a fair age by then and luckily were very strong.

My two neighbours in the village, each with a large dairy of cows to milk, suffered as I did through the water pump. But they did have auxiliary power for the milking machines. In the days when I used to milk cows we used to sit down and milk them out until we got the engine going again. The modern farmer, though, cannot, I believe, milk at all.

The whole affair brought home to me, in no uncertain terms, just how vulnerable our farming is to an interruption in electricity supplies and also how little prepared we are to provide against it. The sensible thing for me to do now is to invest in a generator, of the requisite power, to substitute for the mains. But that would mean quite a big one and ten to one the next emergency would catch us napping again because no one had serviced it.

The interesting thing is that though the snow put our mechanical arrangements into a state of chaos it did little real harm to our grassland and crops. This I believe was because the land had got very dry before it fell, with the surface very hard indeed. The nitrogen we had been spreading was still lying on the surface.

The snow, the equivalent of an inch and a half of rain— 150 tonnes of water an acre, melted gently over the next day or two and in the process warmed the ground up so that growth, which had been very slow, was speeded enormously. At the time of writing in mid-May things don't look too bad. In fact, they look very well indeed. But it is too early to prophesy the harvest with any certainty at all. All I can say is that there will be one.

July 1981   COUNTRY GENTLEMAN

In Defence of Farming

L AST week BBC-2 broadcast a programme entitled 'Butterflies and Barley', which was yet another emotive attack on modern farming systems.

I am all in favour of free speech, but I would have thought the programme could have been balanced by a farming view or at least a rational assessment of what is going on. The general theme was that modern farming was destroying the flora and fauna of the countryside.

Of course it is. But the point insufficiently appreciated by the objectors is that the British countryside has been changing ever since men came to these islands.

The earliest settlements were probably on the chalk downs of the south. These people rooted out the scrub, picked off the stones and made them into boundaries, and then cultivated their tiny fields. These are still visible in most downland areas. It was not until Roman times that the great forests were cleared and the drainage of the swamps begun.

Hedges were not planted until the common field farming of the Middle Ages gave way to the individual farming following the Enclosure Acts. Hedges were planted as field and farm boundaries, and to keep stock at home. Had wire been available in those days there would have been few hedges. I have read accounts written in the 19th century deploring the hedging of Essex fields and lamenting the loss of the broad sweep of undulating country.

Many of the woods are of fairly recent origin, planted during the farming depression following the end of the Napoleonic war. They had an economic use in providing hazel and sweet chestnut for sheep hurdles and thatching spars, materials for which there is little demand these days.

These woods were originally cultivated land. Is there any good reason why they should not be turned back to it again? The point was made that under some provisions of the Countryside Bill farmers would be paid to leave unimproved or unploughed certain specified areas.

I can't see anything wrong in this at all. If I have a block of land which the public wishes to preserve in its original state there is every reason why the public should pay some of the cost of keeping it from being properly farmed.

This particular point concerned Exmoor and it really amounted to preventing the farmer from turning his heather slopes into a reasonable pasture, thereby multiplying its stocking capacity many times.

The conservationists need educating into the benefits of land improvement. There is great satisfaction to my mind in seeing green pastures stocked with thriving sheep instead of black heather where the hungry sheep are infested by ticks.

There is a serious point here. What do the people really want? Is it the distant view or the study of the ecology of a small area of heather? From the ecology or wildlife point of view there are myriads of such places all over the United Kingdom. Every farm has perforce areas of waste in which all sorts of wildlife can flourish. Quite a few farmers even make provision for such places.

For those who want to look on nature in the raw, it is worth remembering that 7m hectares of the country are actually under arable cultivation as against 5m hectares of permanent grass and 6.3m hectares of rough grazing.

November 1981   FINANCIAL TIMES

Farming Lessons

WHEN I left school over 50 years ago and determined to be a farmer the odds, I was told, were heavily against my succeeding. Not only was the world slump beginning and prices falling, but farms were not easy for an outsider to take.

I emigrated for a few years and when I came back things had reached such a pass that landlords were persuading farmers to rent their farms. But, because of the circumstances of the day, arable farms were at a discount and others not much better.

Even so all the wise men were saying that only fools would

take on where experienced men were going bankrupt. That period, 1933 to 1935, was, if we had only realised it at the time, the golden age of farming opportunity. Most of Hampshire could have been bought for about £10 an acre, the problem was finding enough cash to buy more than a small holding.

After 1935 things began to get a bit better and the farm market tightened up. Even so it was possible to buy land at an economic price right through to the early sixties. That is, at a price which would allow the farmer to pay interest charges on the money spent and show a profit.

Since then entry or expansion into farming has been very difficult. Land has been bought for other reasons than its farming value, particularly as a hedge against inflation, for long-term capital gain and because it has been the fashionable thing to do. At the same time the number of farms to let has shrunk, partly through legislation which allows tenancy succession but mainly because at rents paid up to now farming has been profitable. No one wishes to give up a profitable way of life, and in addition the number of tenant farmers is reducing. From 90 per cent at the turn of the century to about 33 per cent today.

This has given rise to the declaration that there are no opportunities left for young men to get into farming. This is manifestly untrue. Farmers are as mortal as anyone else.

The reason why so few farms are becoming vacant for sale is that owner occupiers and some tenants are able to pass them on to their families and these are keen to take them. Fifty years ago many farmer's sons went into other jobs. A career in banking was particularly inviting—providing a 9 to 5 job with a pension at the end. I was considered particularly foolish not to have taken such an opportunity when offered.

But in spite of all the gloom about prospects young men do get into farming, not perhaps by particularly orthodox means but they do show that the opportunities do exist. There is the classic example of Mr Anthony Rosen, who built Fountain Farming from nothing to more than 25,000 acres in the course of a dozen years before the colder financial climate caused him to come unstuck.

There have been other entrepreneurial characters who by various means have gained control of farming empires, though these have not been quite so widely publicised. They have succeeded in selling themselves to the owners of land and capital and so far their systems appear to be working.

But these successes are not the image the general public have in mind. To them a farmer is a man close to the soil, not one who spends his time between an aeroplane and a computer terminal. They believe that for the ordinary young farmer, a practical man of the soil, the opportunities just don't exist.

The Oxford Farming Conference last week provided a refutation of this. Three youngish men described how they had succeeded by a combination of hard work and persistence to succeed in their chosen lines.

Mr Simon Orpwood spent some time looking at farming opportunities in Australia and New Zealand before deciding to have a try in England where he thought his limited capital would have more scope. He did some contracting and then persuaded a landowner to let him 30 acres of land on which to run outdoor breeding sows.

With the help of some friends and suppliers he was able to begin with a herd of 140 sows in 1976 which has expanded to 480. His landlord has the advantage of the pig dung on the land which he ploughs up in his rotation. The secret of Mr Orpwood's success is that his capital is invested in low cost housing for his pigs and in the sows themselves which, farrowing twice a year, provide a very high cashflow.

Mr Tony Hextall who began with 40 cows on an 85-acre smallholding built this up to 150 cows before he was able to move to a 200 acre farm where he has 200 cows. Like Mr Orpwood he invested in animals with a very high cash output and is achieving remarkable results.

Mr Mike Warman began with turkeys in a small way in 1967 and after various vicissitudes he is in charge of marketing a total of 5,000 birds a week in processed form in a company to which he sold his own producing unit.

Fortunately these papers will be published in the Conference Report later this year. They are essential reading for the aspiring young farmer.

January 1982   FINANCIAL TIMES

Memoirs of a Non-hunter

MR Kidd, one of those who objected to my remarks about fox hunting, suggested that I have missed out in life through not being addicted to horses and was good enough to offer me a mount. This I must decline. I gave up professional riding many years ago, as soon as I could get a job and then an occupation that provided me with motorised transport, and have seldom trusted myself to a horse's tender mercies since.

But I had four years in New Zealand and Argentina when I rode every day and all day except when I was doing harder work. Every crease in my trousers gave me sores and I developed piles through riding on a wet saddle. There were no comfortable hot baths after a day on horseback to take out the aches and pains as Mr Kidd doubtless does to relax after a day's hunting. There were no hot baths, only a swim in a creek or a water tank. Neither to be recommended in the winter months.

In New Zealand my employer provided a hack, by name and by nature, a disillusioned beast of burden. I had to ride her six days a week on the farm and could have her for my own pleasure on Sundays. She was my only escape from the lonely farm. I used to ride her five miles to the township where I borrowed a bicycle. A bike will carry one much further than any horse on a main road and does allow for a silent approach while looking out the local talent. The clatter of hooves or neighing will soon alert an anxious parent or brother.

I was supposed to take José, for that was her name, to the annual camp of the mounted rifles into which I had been conscripted. I did my best to militarise her. She stood stock still while I fired a rifle off her back. In fact she stood still for most of the time unless forced along by constant whipping.

I was riding across a boggy stretch over which she was gingerly picking her way when we were attacked by a wild heifer. I tried to make her accelerate, at which her hooves broke through the surface and she bogged down. Horse's hooves are cone shaped; when they go into mud they stay there. A heifer's on the other hand are cloven and squeeze together when pulling out of mud. I jumped off. José suitably lightened was able to

By the time he had learnt how to ride the conventional way he was too saddle sore to do it!

gallop away drawing the heifer after her. She may have saved my life.

The Argentine horses were much more lively. I had half a dozen in my troop, one for every working day. This meant that every morning there was a fresh horse to ride and if I wasn't very careful it would dump me off or try to. I learnt a lot about horses there. That the tamest horse would turn temperamental, that when chasing cattle they could trip and the only thing to do when a horse looked like falling was to abandon ship as fast as possible. I was not as good as the local gauchos who would end up running along the ground, but I never broke anything.

I even had to break in about a dozen in three weeks which had been lassoed out of the mob of youngsters. They were good Argentine stock horses without too much blood line so they could stand our treatment. Rather better than I could, although I always fell off well, perhaps through having played rugby.

Some were used as polo ponies and I had to train them. Once when changing mounts at the end of a chukka I put the bridle on awkwardly and the horse's head came up and broke my nose. I did not rate a groom. The only pleasure ride I suppose was the 25 miles to the nearest town to spend the day with some friends, riding back at night with the horse shying at every imagined sight and sound.

One of my predecessors in this job had been sacked, allegedly for not getting back on a horse that had thrown him. I passed muster on this one, and after doing so handed him over to the transport gang to pull a light cart. Meanwhile one day with the manager I was riding one of my own tamed horses which became upset and began to buck. I had never had such a banging before, and after the third mighty leap I abandoned ship and landed well clear.

He galloped away and I can still see the sardonic look in the manager's eyes as he waited for me to remount. I never did take that test. The horse charged a wire fence and lamed itself so badly that it could not be ridden again. I left before he recovered. Do you blame me?

January 1982   FINANCIAL TIMES

The Courgette Takes Over

TIME was when the courgette, a relative of the cucumber was a luxury product. In fact it does not appear in my gardening encyclopedia. But it is fast taking over the gardens and the deep freezers of rural England. I used at one time to be rather fond of it sliced and fried with good peppering. But now I never want to see one again.

We started with a plant on a bed of pig manure and for a long time nothing happened. The crop grew and flowered just as a marrow used to, and all that was to be seen were a few little cigar-like objects hardly worth picking. Then we were away for a weekend and on our return production burst out of hand.

The courgettes were growing visibly. A Corona-sized one before lunch, would be the size of a large cucumber by tea time and by the next day a foot long and three inches thick. We harvested what we could. Some we ate at once, and others went into the deep freeze or were ground into soup, again for deep freezing. Three times in one week we had them stuffed with minced beef. Just like the marrows which I used to loathe so much at school.

I heard that the local pub would put them on the counter

and sell them, placing the money in the charity box. I chose a moment when I knew the landlady would be out and left a box-full on her doorstep with a note. She was not amused, everyone else in the village had the same idea. It was a classic case of production without thought of market.

I tried feeding them to the sheep but after a suspicious sniff they walked away. On the compost heap they dissolve into a horrid jelly. But what a waste of vegetables into the production of which have gone many man hours of work. Come to think of it they were mainly women hours, and I was given firmly to understand that what we grew in the garden had to be eaten. Just like the nursery.

None of our friends will take any more, although two returning to Washington were induced to take half a dozen. I did not tell them that the US Health Authorities would probably relieve them of them on the grounds of plant health.

The whole trouble is, I think, that the courgette lacks taste appeal. If only the plant breeders could give it the texture of the avocado disposal would be no trouble at all. After all, what is plant breeding all about if not to give the consumer what he wants? In the end I stopped the invasion, chopping off the leaves and reducing the plant to its barest essentials which regretfully are still producing vigorously. In the dusk I pull them off and throw them as far away as I can. Will no one rid me of this vegetable embarrassment?

October 1982   FINANCIAL TIMES

Village Shopping

I HAVE never yet gone shopping in a modern supermarket. In fact I have only once gone into one; in this case it was to look at the sort of job that was being made in presenting meat, a product I am very interested in. I didn't like what I saw, and was walking out through the entry passage when someone stopped me and asked me what I had been buying and saying

I should go out through the pay booths where queues of housewives were waiting patiently.

He was a bit suspicious, so I invited him to call a policeman and my solicitor, and if I was found to have lifted nothing to be prepared to face a charge of wrongful arrest and damages which would keep me in luxury for a good many years. In any case, I told him, such was the poor-looking sample of meat on offer, that I wouldn't steal it, even if my cat was starving. The next time I was in what could be called a mini market. My wife was ill and she gave me her list of things to buy. This shop was in a nearby village and one of the assistants was well known to me, having been brought up in the village. 'Ah Rose,' I said, 'here is Mrs Cherrington's list; I have to go to the bank and will be back in an hour.' When I came back there was a box of groceries on the counter and all I had to do was produce a cheque.

So I have never had to stand in the long lines before the tills which I see through the superstore windows. It is true that the local wives, my own among them, go to be humiliated in this way. If the tills were insufficiently manned and the queue long, I would leave my trolley and walk out. Faced with a couple of hundred abandoned trolleys, the management would soon capitulate. I am sure that Mrs Thatcher wouldn't tolerate it.

But that need not be necessary. In the next village there is always Vera who runs the post office and village shop as did her mother and grandmother. Her shop is open for some time every day of the week so that any forgotten items can be hurriedly secured. Her premises are tiny; a superstore in miniature except that there is no room between the shelves for anyone but Vera and her husband. So one gets counter service of every type of grocery, dry or green. A frozen food cabinet is stuffed to the lid with fish and cooked meats, the selection of cheeses is extensive and the wine list would not disgrace a four-star hotel.

Nor is there the nonsense of wheeling a trolley of groceries across an enormous car park. You park outside, on a corner it is true, but everyone knows that for most of the day there will be half a dozen cars there and drives slowly accordingly. For those needing red meat she cannot cater, but a mile down the road in the next village there is an excellent traditional butcher. What more can anyone need?

It is true that the counter has room for no more than two customers at a time, and those waiting have to exercise patience. But this can be an advantage to those to whom village gossip is the spice of life. At busy times one sometimes has to queue in the rain outside. That is a small price to pay though for the pleasures of real personal service and good quality into the bargain.

Vera's fame has spread far and wide. Not only do the locals call there daily but people from villages miles around and even from the local town. From there housewives drive past the windows of Tesco, Waitrose and even the Co-op disregarding the enticement of bargain offers for the true values of Vera's little shop.

But this is leading to problems. There are rumours, so far unsubstantiated, that her premises are to be much enlarged, that proper shelving will be installed, so that she and her husband will be able to sit at the tills, while the customers do the hard graft of picking and choosing. Think again, dear Vera, think again.

February 1983   FINANCIAL TIMES

Exorcising Fishing

SOME weeks ago I met an old schoolfriend who had in the fullness of time become a bishop and now a retired one. He inquired about my health. Very good, I told him. Then, as appears second nature to a prelate, he became inquisitorial. You seem to have something on your mind, some fundamental worry; your marriage? your family?

I replied that he was right, but it was nothing like that. The fact is that I have an obsession, a craving which I can't resist. He was all attention.

Drink? Gambling? Sex? He is a very broadminded cleric.

The fact is I told him, I have to go salmon fishing. I spend countless hours on rivers and streams flogging them to the point of exhaustion knowing that I may never see a fish, let alone catch one.

I have reasoned out the stupidity of the exercise that the chances of catching one are about one in a million casts, and that with the decline in salmon stocks the odds are getting longer every day. But still I persist.

Could you not, with your great wisdom and experience, exorcise this demon from me? Exorcism was I thought part of a priest's basic training. It was not on any curriculum he told me but most in his calling had had a shot at it during their ministry, on an amateur basis, of course. 'But,' he went on, 'yours is a difficult case. Most vices and obsessions are founded on pleasurable sensations in the first place.

'Thanks to their early religious training most people have a guilty conscience about enjoying themselves and an exorcist often gets the best results by playing on these subconscious themes.

'But in your case things are very different. Salmon fishing by every account appears to be a form of self torture which we only see in Indian Fakirs lying on beds of nails. When in India I found it impossible to make such people see any reason at all. They don't seem to feel any pain. Do you?'

'I certainly do,' I said. 'I am often wet, I get very tired, the hooks stick into my ears and hands. I talk of nothing but fishing in the brief moments when I am not in the water. I know it's a mug's game but I still can't give it up.'

'Your poor fellow,' he said, 'I will try. But I can't promise anything.' Two days later I caught a fish, and this of course spurred me on, and then for two months things on the Wye got steadily worse. The river dropped and got warmer and several weeks passed without anyone catching a fish at all.

I gradually gave up going there at all. Previously I had insisted in fishing even in impossible conditions.

So fortified I took my wife to Scotland. We had been once this year but I had imprisoned her in a cottage with five other fishermen for about ten days.

She was suspicious especially when she noticed my rods in the boot. I explained it was all part of the cure. A real test of my resolution, like an untouched whisky bottle in a drunkard's cupboard.

And the cure worked. We stayed in a couple of fishing hotels, and I smugly watched the poor saps returning empty-handed every evening. I saw numerous promising rivers and passed them without a pang.

They were down to bare bones of rocks. No fish could have navigated them. The bishop had obviously done his stuff with the weather.

Then on my way home I called in on the Wye. Yes, it had livened up. I decided to fish. After two hours in the boat I was soaked to the skin and hadn't seen or felt a fish.

With great self sacrifice I gave my place to a younger man and went off to change and get warm. He caught a fish.

In the afternoon he suggested that I should fish from the bank and there were fish there. I saw three or four continually. For three hours I fished them without respite, using every kind of bait, legal of course. To no avail. But 100 yards up river he caught another where none was seen at all.

I drove home in cold fury at my stupidity in mortifying my flesh to the extent that I had. I determined to give away my rod next day but found no takers.

It would be a pity to waste it so I rang the ghillie the night before. 'The river is in flood and impossible,' he said. I breathed a sigh of relief. The bishop seems to be winning.

October 1983   FINANCIAL TIMES

Those New Villagers

SOME years ago a farmer of my acquaintance built brand new houses for his workers and to set off some of the cost he sold the old ones to someone who wanted a weekend retreat. The new owner rebuilt the row of cottages into something of a mansion and then resold it to a retired industrialist.

Then the trouble started. You see the farmer had a large herd of pigs, and with the best will in the world one cannot deny

that pigs will cause a smell. The new owner, being retired, had nothing to do with his time but sniff the country air. Which, when the wind was blowing from the piggery, could be said to be offensive. Offensive that is to anyone not actively involved in pig husbandry.

The farmer took little notice of the complaints at first, and when taxed with it said that the original purchaser had bought with his eyes, or should one say his nose open, and knew well that when the wind was in the south west, as it frequently is in Britain, there would be a smell. The complainant persisted with what the farmer considered to be his harassment, putting sanitary and other officials on his trail. To the farmer's dismay his excuse that the pigs were in the district first was only grudgingly accepted by the officials and there was talk of action being taken through the courts.

In the end a compromise was reached. The farmer at great expense installed a sort of giant scent spray which automatically discharged a violet perfume into the atmosphere. But this did not quite satisfy the house owner. It seems that when the pigs were smelling strongly, as they do from time to time, their smell mixed with the perfume made the overall scent even worse, at least according to the man's wife. She came to the farmhouse to complain that it was now like that in a Tunisian brothel. When the farmer asked her how she recognised the smell, she walked off in high dudgeon. They haven't spoken since, and the complaints were redoubled.

Eventually the farmer succumbed to the pressure and moved his pigs to another part of the farm, assisted in this by a grant from the European Community. As it was an improvement he was able to double his output of pig meat and of manure. This he proceeded to spread in his fields which, coincidentally, almost surrounded the new house. Never had these fields been so well tended. But although the complaints started once more and the officials came to harass him, they had to admit he was carrying out acts of husbandry, which he had a perfect right to do.

The moral of this is not that a farmer always wins in the end, but that people who come to live in the country should look closely at their surroundings before they sign their contracts and should also realise that the country is the farmers' work place. This is the case now that most villages have become suburbs populated by commuters or geriatrics.

Fifty years ago the majority of villagers were either actively involved in farming or its supportive skills—thatchers, saddlers, smiths and so on—or they were retired from it. They understood the why's and wherefore's of farming operations, and made allowances for them. Some might well have been cowed into an acceptance of the intrusion of farming into their consciousness because their jobs or houses depended on farmers. But on the whole they realised that they were part of the overall rural pattern.

Not any longer. A sizeable element of the new generation of village dwellers believe that the land the other side of the garden fence is part of their birthright, on which they, their children, their dogs and their horses can be exercised and their rubbish thrown. These are not the vandals from the housing estates who can if caught be dealt with according to the law. But thoroughly respectable middle-class suburbanites who have to be dealt with so tactfully that it raises the farmers' blood pressure to the limit.

These people constitute a greater threat to a farmer's freedom to do what he thinks best for his business than do the conservationists. After all, if a farmer has on his land a registered site of scientific or other interest he will be compensated for leaving it derelict or unimproved. But there is no compensation for the farmer who bows to the pressures of the new generation of village dwellers. Why can't they just go back to the urban fringe?

November 1983   FINANCIAL TIMES

Taking a Horse from Water

HAVING spent what should have been the four best years of my life on horseback in the wide open spaces, and suffered the misery these creatures can inflict on mankind, I was happy to see the last of them disappear from my farm at the end of the war. Their main defect is their unreliability as a form of transport. They also go lame at the drop of a hat, and will seldom behave sensibly when ill.

Nor do I much care for swimming pools in England's climate: they need a lot of maintenance and expensive heating to give you less stimulation than a cold shower does at a fraction of the cost. So I have neither horse nor pool at home. Not so a neighbour, a week-ender who has both. And these two joined together in quite an event the other day.

One of my men met me in the yard. 'Mr Smith's horse is in his swimming pool, I am going to sling it out with a tractor hoist,' he said. Now my early training had taught me that slinging a horse off the ground is a ticklish operation—the horse's back might get broken—and should only be undertaken with the proper tackle. I had dim memories of army King's Regulations on the subject. But I had faced a similar situation in the distant past when one of my cows had fallen into a small reservoir. In her case I had gradually filled the reservoir with straw and she had walked around as it built up, and walked out when she reached ground level.

So I went to the horse scene and took charge. The horse was standing quietly up to its belly in water with its head held by a dedicated horsewoman, with chattering teeth. It had tried to walk across the pool's canvas cover and fallen through, and had had the (momentary) sense or the luck to reach the shallow end. I had a heap of very wet straw bales and sent for them.

But they were not wet enough and instead of sinking formed a raft which we could not sink. There was no chance of emptying the pool as the pump had been dismantled for the winter. The alternative would have been pig dung of which I had a big heap and which would have made a ramp. But what would Mr Smith think of ten tonnes of the stuff in his pool? While deliberations were continuing a lorry came for the sheep. The driver was a part-time fireman. Dial 999, he advised, ask for the fire brigade and they would have that pool emptied in a trice.

THAT'S ODD, HE JUMPS BEAUTIFULLY AT GYMKHANAS

This brought results. Within about 20 minutes not one but two vehicles arrived complete with portable pumps. It must have been a slack day for arsonists. After a while the water level sank far enough for the bales to rest on the bottom. But we still had to get the horse up a four-foot sheer side. Pools in the country should in future be built with a sloping ramp at the shallow end.

We built the ramp with bales and tried to make the animal step on it. This it refused to do. The water was now only about a foot up its legs and I doubt if it even felt cold. Also it was showing a bit of sense. Few horses are really sure-footed. They have little grip in their hooves, unlike a cloven hooved creature like a cow which can tackle very difficult places. That is why bullock teams were used by the pioneers.

So into the pool went the husky firemen and shoved. The small daughter of the house offered it some nuts and it scrabbled to the top unharmed. It was a very lucky creature, first because the pool held enough water to break its fall, then that the fire brigades will go to any lengths to save an animal—usually kittens in trees. But particularly, I think, because the very stupidity that led it to walk on the canvas cover made it so thick that unlike most horses it did not lose its head as they so often do under stress.

There is a moral in this. If you have both a horse and a swimming pool make sure the first can't escape and that the pool is well fenced to keep horses and every thing else from falling in.

That evening the brigade chief rang me up. 'I am writing my report,' he said. 'What is the horse's name?' 'I don't know,' I replied, 'I never asked it.'

December 1983   FINANCIAL TIMES

Christmas Feasts

MY first experience of what might be called the nitty-gritty of the Christmas season was as a farm boy in New Zealand. There were two or three turkeys round the yard and I was deputed to kill one and prepare it for the feast. I had never done this before; but my boss was a man of uncertain temper and I knew he would have given me a roasting for Pommy incompetence. So, I decided to have a go.

I thought it would not be too hard. After all, and with my boss's temper in mind, I had already learnt how to wring a chicken's neck quite effectively, to say nothing of slaughtering ducks and sheep. I reasoned that a turkey would be no worse—only bigger.

I was wrong. It was far too strong for my inexperienced hands. There was but one thing to do: I took it to the back of the wool shed and blew off its head with a .303 rifle.

There remained to pluck the bird, and I hung it up and went to work. It was rather tough, though, and I wore my fingers to the bone pulling out the feathers as well as tearing the skin.

At this stage the boss (whom I suspected knew as little as I did) appeared on the scene and took over. After a few minutes, he lost his temper. 'You have ruined it, boy,' he roared. Out came his knife and he skinned it. Actually, because his wife was a good cook the result was not too bad; and the stuffing and sausage meat were just as well at the side of the plate as sewn into the bird. 'After all,' said the boss 'it is more sanitary this way.'

I never skinned a turkey; but I wished I had when a friend gave us a goose for Christmas. The bird was delivered dead and I set to work plucking it. Now, a goose's plumage grows in two parts: the external feathers and the down. The feathers came away quickly enough but the down defeated me, and the bird I handed to my wife looked like a bad case of seven o'clock stubble. She decided to singe it off and held it over a tin bath of burning newspaper. The flames waxed exceedingly, scorched her hands, and the bird fell into the fire, from which it was rescued with difficulty.

The charred skin added a certain cachet to the feast but we found that the goose is a most disappointing bird. Had I skinned it first, there would have been little left on the carcase and most of the flavour would have gone.

This reminds me of my first Christmas in Argentina where, 50 years ago, eating red meat was the way of life. The Christmas treat for the staff of the *estancia* where I was working was 'Asado con Cuero' (roast in the skin). A couple of big calves were spitted over an open fire, with the skins away from the heat. This process ensured that all the natural juices were kept in the flesh, and we gorged ourselves on the tender meat without benefit of plates or vegetables.

This *estancia* was one of the last traditional ones in the area where the owners liked to carry on the old life. My next Christmas was on a much more businesslike establishment where every beast had to be accounted for to head office in Buenos Aires.

So, this Christmas the treat was a half-grown porker cooked

whole on the fire using the technique described by Charles Lamb in his dissertation on roast pig. In fact, it lay among the flames until the cook, one of the *estancia* hands, pronounced it ready. Such was his culinary skill that I suspected he could have been one of the reasons our pig herd never grew any larger.

Some years ago, I was invited to a Christmas party at a friend's home in Jamaica. I soon realised that the invitation was not entirely disinterested when, as soon as I arrived, the host led me to the garden where a large pig was lying in a pit surrounded by wood.

As a farmer, he said, you must know about these things: please roast it for us. Thus, I spent most of the evening doing that aided by one or two enthusiastic amateurs (whom I suspected knew more than I did). Just before midnight we pronounced it ready, dragged it from the fire and cut hunks off for the guests. They just about devoured it; but as they had been drinking steadily for about four hours, they must have had little appreciation for what was put before them. After all, hunger makes the best sauce.

December 1983 FINANCIAL TIMES

Alongside the humour, JOC's grasp of events was formidable. He demonstrated this when he analysed agricultural politics for farmers overseas.

The NFU and the Government

IF you remember your Shakespeare Julius Caesar was murdered on the Ides of March after disregarding the soothsayer's awful warnings.

British farmers have been taking all too much notice of dire prophecies, but unlike Caesar are rather apathetically expecting the worst, while calling stridently for help in every direction and vigorously attacking almost everything in sight.

One of their main targets is the present National Farmers' Union leadership. Farmers' relationships with their union are pretty ambivalent. Most of them belong as a sort of insurance policy, rather like membership of the established church which does ensure a decent burial.

Insurance of another sort comes into it, because the NFU Mutual Insurance will see to it that their clients are well serviced in all the day to day difficulties of insurance. At the same time the network branch and county secretaries depend for their income on the commissions earned from premiums.

When things are going well, as they have been until recently, few farmers bother to attend meetings and the representation on the union's committees at local and national level is mainly formed by what might be called committee types starting a political life. In this they are assisted by the fact that there is still very good labour to be had for farms, and also there is usually a supply of sons anxious to see the old man out of the way at meetings etc. without worrying too much about the home front.

The NFU is credited with being the most effective lobby operating in Britain with powers to influence governments. This claim is rather far fetched to say the least and is now shown to be an illusion. When the NFU was most in the public eye was when the government of the day used it as an instrument of its policy.

Prewar governments took little notice, and the NFU was run on a shoe string. But then all of a sudden the conservative government of the day plucked the president of the NFU from the union and made him Minister of Agriculture.

Why did the government take this unprecedented step? Far from seeing the virtues of Sir Reginald Dorman Smith the government feared that it was going to lose a crucial by-election where a very popular farmer politician was standing in opposition to the Conservatives and they might have lost. So the NFU had a Minister and the independent withdrew.

After the war began the government decided that home food production was a priority and brought the NFU in as an agent to ensure that this policy worked. This was further developed after the war and the links between Whitehall and the NFU were very close indeed.

It was rather an interesting situation as until food became plentiful towards the end of 1956 the combined effort of government and NFU was to keep prices down, although the then leadership of the NFU tried to convince their members that they were keeping prices up.

In truth had farmers been more businesslike they would have used the scarcity to squeeze the last ounce out of the consumer.

During this period the links between the union and the Ministry were close, almost as thick as treacle, and this continued during the run up to joining the EEC. There was an annual review of the industry on which the guaranteed prices were fixed, and by and large the farmers did not do so badly.

EEC membership has changed all that. By the time that we became full members the Ministry became the interpreter of EEC policy. All the decisions had to be made in Brussels which could override British wishes.

This meant that even the pretence of NFU influence with government was by permission of the EEC and the union had to find another target, in Brussels.

This they did by joining COPA, the European farm lobby comprising all national unions. But here they found themselves in unfamiliar territory.

COPA has no say with the Council of Ministers and has little say over the actions of its members. However separate members have great power with their own governments. How else do you suppose that French farmers can riot unchecked on their roads and railways?

The simple answer is that in Britain farmers are only 2 per cent of the population while in France they are about 10 per cent and in the rest of the EEC rather more.

By handing over responsibility to Brussels and keeping strictly to EEC law the government had a wonderful alibi for whatever it did.

Mr Peter Walker the former Minister was a bit in the European mould and did one or two rather doubtful deals, just like a French Minister might but Mr Jopling, the present Minister, is of a different stamp. He is strictly legal and shows no initiative at all.

Our own farming policy is made by the Treasury and the Foreign Office under the direction of Mrs Thatcher who is basically against the Community and most certainly against the Common Agricultural Policy which she wants to see reformed.

The whole of Ministry policy now is to the effect that farming is costing too much and that everyone should contribute to lowering these expenses. In any case, they argue, the general British public is fed up with farmers who spend their time despoiling the countryside and choking the atmosphere by burning straw.

So Sir Richard Butler and the other leaders of the union are finding themselves in the frustrating position of having plenty of complaints from their members but being able to do nothing about them because the Minister's every reply is to refer to Brussels.

Mr Jopling has done better than that by going off to Australia and New Zealand for a fortnight with his key officials, so avoiding any contact with the NFU during their annual meeting.

I don't say this was deliberate strategy but it was certainly an odd time to have chosen, and this is where the Ides of March comes into it. You see the fate of the CAP is supposed to be settled by a summit meeting at the end of March.

There are all sorts of meetings going on in the EEC to try and work something out but the main British link is going to be down under and unable to look after the interests of the farmers. Nor is he going to be in Britain to receive the representations of the NFU.

Because of the lack of communication all we have to go on is rumour, but it looks at present that returns for milk and cereals could be down around 10 per cent as would be beef and lamb. This has led Sir Richard to claim that British farming is sliding into recession. This is palpable nonsense for anyone like me who remembers what sliding into recession was really like.

At the same time the NFU membership has woken from its complacency and is busy attacking the president for failing to change the government's mind, for having no influence with the Minister and, far worse in their eyes, for allowing an attack on farming to have developed in the press and on television.

This media attack has really met with a response with the

public. I called on an aunt of mine in her ninety-ninth year the other day and she asked me when I was going to stop piling up surpluses and burning down the countryside.

The general public is also very aware that farmers have done well, while many of them have suffered the monetarist antics of Mrs Thatcher. They see no reason for any tenderness towards farmers and I really believe that a majority would like to see us suffer.

Farmers have convinced themselves the Community reforms are going to be applied ruthlessly in Britain because of our dislike of the illegal. That would be bad enough. But there is a scenario that would point to a Community policy which returned the responsibility for farming to national governments.

With surpluses about and the government in its present mood this is the stuff of nightmares. My guess is that it could come about.

March 1984   NEW ZEALAND FARMER

In March 1984 the British Farmer and Stockbreeder *came to an end. JOC had written for it and its predecessor,* Farmer and Stockbreeder, *for 26 years.*

The End of BF&S

THE end of *British Farmer and Stockbreeder* is sad for me. I have been a reader of the magazine (in its various forms) for more than fifty years and I wrote part of a column called 'Blythe' as one of my first essays into journalism. Blythe was a composite character, and I never quite knew who my co-authors were. He could be very practical, and I remember him holding forth at length about the Rouen system.

This was the practice of leaving a certain amount of summer growth on a pasture for the cattle to graze overwinter: an essential part of inter-war dog-and-stick farming. In fact I originally took my farm here at Tangley on a grazing tenancy because the landlord had left a summer's grass on it.

I saw nothing wrong with dog and stick. In fact, such training as I had had in New Zealand and elsewhere was in the nature of ranching. I could not see this succeeding in those pre-war years on less than about 2,000 acres. So, until I had built up to that area, I was milking cows on two Hosier bails.

By the time the war started I was more than half way to my goal, but then I was forced by circumstances to reduce the cows and other livestock and become an arable farmer. Once you become locked in the system—any system—it seems to be impossible to break out unless there is a catalyst like a war to force the change. So I am still in a mainly arable groove and unlikely, unless forced, to de-intensify.

It's worth remembering that the pre-war slump was simply the continuation of the removal of the duties on grain which began to have its impact in the 1870s. This led to a steady deterioration of arable farming away from the best lands, with a slight uplift during the food scarcities of the 1914 war.

At the end of that war there was in existence a guarantee system, the Corn Production Act, which provided fixed prices. This was cancelled in June 1921 and prices for almost everything halved. In addition there was a monumental drought. This depression was at its worst in 1932–33. Since then, things have gradually improved.

If you study farming history, these past fifty years have been the longest cycle of farming prosperity this country has ever seen. It was faltering a bit in the late sixties, but joining the Common Market produced a new boost to profitability.

I know that the pundits claim that in real terms incomes are not what they were a few years ago; but what I, like most farmers, regard as real terms are today's prices for what I sell and what I buy.

Of particular interest to me is what is going to happen over the next few months or years. At just about the time this is published, the heads of the EEC should be holding a summit in Brussels. There will be a great deal at stake both for farming and for the government. Mrs Thatcher is determined to reduce Britain's contribution to the Community. Will she get her way?

She is in a strong position. She is threatening to withhold her payments as well as refusing any increase in the EEC's own resources. In addition she is showing every sign of being anti-farmer, not only where the Europeans are concerned but at home as well.

Mrs Thatcher is also demanding that the Common Agricultural Policy must be reformed: which means that it is not to cost so much. She is in a position to enforce this simply by refusing to sign the cheques.

This cost control is crucial. We have already felt its effects in the delays in grant payments. If there is no settlement this month, the EEC will run out of cash by August.

At best there would be payment delays, at worst limited intervention and exporting, which is already starting. Our European colleagues might well start rioting, but of course we shan't. There are too few of us. Other member countries will no doubt aid their farmers. The whole Community could adopt national measures. I know some say that if this were to happen it would be the end of European unity, but very few people really believe that the future of Europe lies in feather-bedding its farmers.

A much more rational assessment of the future is that, if the CAP looks to be collapsing now, the entry of Spain and Portugal will destroy it completely. The potential for the expansion of Spanish farming, once the European borders are open to her, is enormous.

The alternative to national policies is for a system like that in the US, where there are common prices all over. This has driven farming to the better lands, leaving millions of potential farming acres derelict. Apply that to Western Europe and see how much of British farming could survive!

I believe that 1984 will be the turning point of the 50-year cycle. I doubt if there will be a 'big bang' disintegration of the CAP on the lines of the 1921 debacle. What is most likely is a slow erosion of it into a mixture of community and national measures. It's obvious that production of beef, cereals and milk will have to be curbed. It is also obvious that the only agency capable of making a restrictive policy work would be the member states' own governments.

There will also have to be some protection against the excess production of other member states. This, again, is anathema to the European idealists. Here I would like to repeat what the late Asher Winegarten once said to me. He believed that the CAP as it was drafted, far from fostering European unity, would be the agent of its destruction. It didn't seem sensible to impose such an inflexible strait-jacket of a policy on as varied a social, climatic and agricultural scene as that of Europe.

On one of my first visits to Brussels more than 25 years ago I asked one of the first officials I met how long it would be before Europe was completely integrated, let alone united. It will take at least a century, was his reply. I am sure he was right.

This is why I believe that for a long time to come there will be no certainty in the CAP. It will exist in name, but it will probably be a sort of agricultural association within a tariff wall against other countries.

My great regret is that I shan't live to see what will really happen, but then I don't think many of you will either. However, I intend to go on taking an interest in it all, as I have up till now.

Anyway, thank you for reading me, for your many letters and your kindnesses when I have met you. Good luck and good farming!

March 1984   BRITISH FARMER AND STOCKBREEDER

As one door closed, another opened. Even before his pen was dry from finishing the preceding article, JOC started writing for Farming News. *Although he was well into his seventies, his appetite for day-to-day farming was as keen and fresh as ever. Much of his* Farming News *column was devoted to Tangley Farm. 1984 turned out to be one of his best years ever, but after 50 years of farming, JOC never counted on anything until it was in the barn.*

The Farming Year

2nd MARCH

I missed the NFU AGM and enjoyed instead a very good week of farming weather. There was a lot of frost, but the sun shone and by afternoon the fallows had softened enough to let the spring-tine harrows in to break the soil.

By the next afternoon this cultivated land worked well and at the end of the week I had most of my spring barley planted.

All I have left is a small field where the sheep are running and 40 acres of peas. Somehow I didn't think mid-February was a good time to plant the peas. The field is heavy and rain in March could have capped the soil.

But of course if it didn't rain for months I shall probably regret it.

The land worked down surprisingly well considering the fact that we had six inches of rain in January. I had put a good tilth down to the fact that I had subsoiled one field last autumn only to find that the area which did not receive this treatment worked just as well.

The winter wheat all looks well and shows no sign of discoloration. Some of it is strong enough to graze as it would hide a hare in March, but somehow the practice has been dropped. I don't think there have been any experiments to prove that grazing wheat affects yields, but the neighbours would certainly talk if I started feeding off one of my fields. Some of them get very excited if they just notice one of my sheep on a 100-acre field.

30th MARCH

I have just about finished lambing and it has not been a vintage one this time.

After the first 25 per cent, numbers dropped have recovered to normal—about 80 per cent multiple births—but the earlier shortfall will take some making up.

I also had far too many barreners and this was partly my own fault. Last year some 10 per cent of the new flock entrants did not breed a lamb.

We thought that this was out of line and decided to keep them for another year but most of them still failed to lamb. So it was not the fault of the ram, the ewes were just naturally non-breeders.

There were a few more prolapses than usual and the first lambers were very scary for some reason—thinking that dropping one lamb and then decamping with it was their duty done.

We caught and brought in most of these, but we had a lot of trouble doing this as 70 per cent of the flock took the ram in the same week making it impossible to get the lambing ewes inside.

Normally lambing is outside in a number of small paddocks rotating the flock as necessary. As with these numbers this was impossible, I put the lambing ewes on some very good ryegrass and kept them in the field to lamb.

They were very quiet as we did not have to feed and lambed well. Fortunately too the weather, although cold, was dry.

After all this I am making the following resolutions:

- To look into the possibilities of determining ewe pregnancy about the turn of the year.

- To find a method of restricting the numbers taking the ram to about 25 per cent of the flock every week without harm to the flock's fertility.
- Going back to my practice of lambing the two-tooths separately from the main flock and at a different time, without detriment to the percentages.
- And making provision to bring the flock inside at nights if it becomes really necessary.

I am still hesitant about indoor lambing. My experience is that the major losses in lambs over a couple of days old are among those which have been inside in spite of disinfectants and antibiotic sprays.

My major success has been a hundred acres of RVP Italian ryegrass sown last August. It was grazed twice in the winter, top-dressed February 7 and is now growing away from rather more than six ewes an acre.

27th APRIL

After a holiday in Northern Brittany I came home in mid April hoping that spring had arrived in my absence. But I was quite wrong. It's true that the winter corn was a nice green colour but it had not really grown much; the spring barley could have been in the ground three weeks and not nine and the pastures were just a bit greener than they had been when I left. The only real growth had been on the RVP leys which were still carrying nearly seven ewes and their lambs an acre after a month.

The problem undoubtedly has been a combination of night frosts and lack of rain. Although there is quite a lot of moisture in the clay soil, the surface is getting very hard and baked. I doubt if there will be much movement in the cereals until there is a nice soak and a bit more warmth and no more night frosts. Daytime temperatures approaching 60 degrees are easily undone by night frosts.

In fact it is all rather like the springs that we used to have when April was a dry month and there would be a howling NE wind as well. Luckily we have been spared that so far. Otherwise the weather was exactly right for land work, fertilising and rolling and even a bit of spraying. It's all so different from last year, when every operation was rained off and the lambs never had a dry coat for most of the spring. But this does not mean that the harvest will be anything approaching last year's, which was the best I have ever had for winter corn.

To begin with, one field of wheat has a very poor plant. It is on some of my best land and follows a ley down for six years and with a very good textured soil. The culprit was either wireworm or leatherjacket which did not do quite enough damage to make me plough it up but will leave me with an eye-sore. One other field has some waterlogged patches where heavy rain caught us out when drilling. How I envy those who farm light friable land. They should pay a special levy to help the clay and flint men.

In fact both my bad patches are on leys and it makes me wonder if the grass break which I stick to not very religiously is essential in this enlightened age. The trouble is that in this part of the world there is not much else. Peas I have found terribly unreliable. You either get a massive crop which is difficult to harvest and with a blackened sample suffering maximum deductions, or a nice clean green result but a yield so low that I wished I had stuck to spring barley.

In any case I am rather doubtful of the residual benefits of a pea crop. You do get a nice seed bed and a good opening burst of fertility and then somehow it does not last. You may save nitrogen on growing the actual pea crop but you certainly want to use it on the subsequent wheat. I once had the most dreadful attack of fusarium—at least that was what was diagnosed—on wheat after peas. I shall have a good test this year. Two-thirds of a 50-acre field are wheat after peas with the balance the fifth wheat crop. At the moment it is difficult to spot the dividing line. It will be interesting to see what happens at the end.

11th MAY

Because of the peculiarities of publishing I have to write this 10 days before it appears. At this time I am deeply pessimistic after more than four weeks of drought. I have been making my apprehension worse by looking up historical facts about previous drought years.

If by the time you read this we have had a good soak, save it up for the next barren spring. If we haven't I shall be halfway round the bend.

'An abnormally dry year with almost unparalleled drought. January mild but rainy. February very dry. March showery. April dry with cold spell. May fine and dry. June and July unbroken drought. August below average rainfall.'

The above is an extract from the book *Agricultural Records* and goes on to mention that harvest was abnormally early and wheat yields were good. As an afterthought, it mentions that the Government of the day repealed the Corn Production Act which guaranteed prices with the result that the price of wheat fell from £15 to £10 a tonne.

So far, by the beginning of May, the Hampshire climate has behaved just like this. Six inches of rain in January and none in February to speak of. Two and a bit inches in March and none at all since.

So far the Government, or rather the EEC Commission, has not reduced wheat prices by 33 per cent as its predecessors did.

The previous attack on prices was made by Liberal–Tory coalition. Many farmers had a very rough time in that and subsequent years, particularly those who had started up at the high prices ruling at the end of the 1914–18 war.

I remember an old Sussex farmer telling me that he took over from his father in February 1921, planted his barley and it never had a rain until long after a very light harvest.

By then the horse teams and dairy cows had fallen to less than a third of the take-over value.

He told me he paid his father interest on the money until in the mid-thirties his father died and he inherited the debt which he thankfully wrote off.

It was fortunate for him that he had a father as a creditor, banks would not have been able to be so generous.

I am particularly interested in the statement that wheat yields were very good.

In my first harvest year—1934, another very dry summer, they were the same—about a tonne an acre.

But lately I have found that dry summers are not necessarily forerunners of high wheat and other cereal yields. It seems to me that the modern wheat crops need a great deal of rain and so does winter barley.

There is a good reason for this in that now crops are so much thicker with much higher yields of grain and straw. Few people realise that it used to be considered good practice to hand-hoe winter wheat. In Holland I saw it being horse-hoed in the early 1960s.

I have this in mind when I look at my own crops just now. They are as thick as I have ever seen them and of quite a good colour.

But during the warm spell in the last two weeks of April their vigorous growth must have exhausted much of the soil moisture.

I have been pulling up plants and finding nothing but dust underneath. The roots also seem to be very shallow. It used to be said that wheat roots went down as far as the ear rose above the ground but they don't seem to be doing so.

It could be that the plants have been spoiled by having all their food put close to the surface. Why should the roots go questing deep into the subsoil for sustenance when it has been handed to them on a plate?

It's also well to remember that until a few years ago wheat used to be part of a rotation and followed a build-up of fertility designed to make it the cash crop of the cycle.

Today rotations are simply disregarded and many of us are practising a form of hydroponics. This is very successful where there is ample moisture to command, as with irrigation, but the British climate is one of the more unreliable irrigators that I know.

It is either too wet or too dry.

As always at this time of dry weather most of the lambs have done very well indeed.

I weighed some the other day, born in the first week of March, and one was already 70 lb with many over 60 lb.

They will, I hope, start to go by mid-May. Their grass is still growing a little and they spend much of their time lying stretched out in the sun. The only disappointing flock is made up of couples which were inside for various reasons.

There is no watery mouth which I have heard about, but some of them have died with symptoms which I would have called those of pulpy kidney.

Others have just not done. But the vet laboratory has not yet come up with an answer.

We also had far too many barreners, although all the sheep had been marked and had had at least two cycles with the rams.

The only explanation I have is that the enormous rush we had in the second week of mating had exhausted some of the rams. There were 2 per cent rams and that should have been enough.

Anyway it will be a stimulus to better management next year. I am glad, though, that mine came in the first 10 days of March for the most part. As many of them as possible will have to be sold by mid-June before the price drops under the floor.

25th MAY

We had well under half an inch of rain the other night, the first significant fall for six weeks and it seemed to freshen things up. The day before I had walked through several fields of winter barley and wheat, making myself miserable pulling plants up and finding no moisture in the roots. Three days after the rain the soil was quite damp to the touch and the roots seemed to be looking a little healthier.

Even the peas had visibly grown about an inch. I had been advised to spray them against thrips and whether this treatment stimulated them or not I don't know.

The rest of the crops look to be surviving well, especially the winter barley just coming into ear and as thick as I have known it on this farm. There are no signs of disease; probably it has been too cold for the fungi to develop as yet. I am a firm believer in keeping the sprayer locked up in the shed unless there is a visible disease to be sprayed.

An interesting facet of the season is that from what I see of my neighbours' farms, early sowing—and in particular early top dressing—seems to have paid off. I have been monitoring one particular wheat field which I pass every week and it was being top dressed in early February. I have always believed that nitrogen on winter corn before March is an invitation to leaching but this year I was wrong.

I had flu early in the month and asked my shepherd to weight off the lambs which had been born from the last week of February onwards. I told him to mark anything over 30 kilos,

65 lbs. I reckoned that a good single lamb at that weight would kill out at around 35 lbs and come to over £40. I expected that he would find about a dozen, just enough to start to lubricate the cash flow.

I wouldn't believe him when he told me that he had marked nearly a third and that one or two had reached 80 lbs. I went to the slaughterhouse to see them weighed and they averaged 37 lbs and ranged from 32 to 48 lbs. I even had four rejected for being over fat and on examination I agreed that they were.

Several of the lambs were twins and none of them could have been older than 10 weeks, some in fact were born in March. I came home from the slaughterhouse and immediately went through two more flocks and drew another load. I have not had the weights at the time of writing. They were all good solid lambs but I doubt if they will be as heavy.

These three lots of sheep had been on Italian ryegrass leys since they were born and had eaten them to the ground; it had been dry almost all their lives.

In fact when we had the rain, which was heavy the other night, the lambs were quite upset. I always think that a sheep does best when it is eating the grass which grew in the night but it is the first time that it has really worked.

10th JUNE

After a fortnight in Wales and Scotland I came home to find the farm looking better than ever. It was a decided contrast to the state I had left it in. Then the situation had been saved by about an inch of rain which got the grass moving again and perked up the corn a little.

Since then we have had another three inches and everything looks wonderful. I am sure the nitrogen sown during the drought and earlier had failed to work, nor had it leached away.

The winter barley which was in ear when I left, and which I thought would be dead and ready to harvest by mid-June, has grown another six inches and looks a good month off harvest.

There is no sign of ripening at the time of writing and I hope the grains will fill out. There is plenty of foliage. The only blemish is some loose smut, not enough to reduce yield significantly but enough to make me buy some fresh seed.

This was sown from my own growing and had been treated with Baytan and showed no sign of smut last year.

The greatest change was in the wheat, particularly the Rapier which had been showing signs of stress as I said a month ago. You would not think it the same crop now and there is no difference between liquid and solid nitrogen.

There are no signs of any disease on the flag leaves, and the Armada which had been sprayed for septoria is looking good. Any further fungicide spraying will be dependent on seeing something to spray. I don't think there is any evidence that prophylactic treatment works on cereals.

During my absence my shepherd had been busy drawing lambs, and by the middle of June a third of the crop will have to be sold.

Then there will have to be a stop until the fall in the guaranteed price can be overcome by the rise in weight.

A 16 kilo lamb was worth £39 on the hook last week. A lamb will need to be at least 19 kilos in weight to reach the same money in a month's time.

The grass has recovered marvellously and now looks as though it was early May in a particularly good year. I doubt though if it has quite the goodness of May grass.

Although the lambs had all been wormed in the last fortnight, several are showing signs of scour, as are the ewes. No doubt the lush grazing is proving too strong for their digestions which have been used to very short commons indeed.

6th JULY

Although I believe the winter barley is now safe to make a good crop, I am not yet sure of the wheat which seems to be getting very dry and on some shallow patches there are definite signs of drought stress with flag leaves twisting upwards.

In spring barley, ear emergence is a little spasmodic in the same sort of places.

I never think barley which ripens in the sheath is very high yielding.

I have been listening to a lot of propaganda to the effect that spring barley will be so short that maltsters will be crawling around with bags of gold trying to persuade us to sell it to them.

These sorts of prophecies never come off.

It is true that a shortage of suitable grain will often make them see reason. But it would be better to make sure of the shortage first before counting our chickens.

If it doesn't rain before harvest—I am writing in the last week of June—we should get the shortage of spring barley, but no doubt then they will change to Igri.

20th JULY

I hadn't meant to make any hay at all but the extraordinary grass growth in this part of England since the end of May meant that I had to. Plus of course the fact that I had sold nearly half the lambs and the farm looks to be half stocked. I never have thought that seeding grass was much good for grazing and I expected that my remaining lambs would gently grow into good stores, although if the drought goes on much longer there will not be much trade for them.

I thought the lambs were doing very well and last week put my hand on a few in the yards. To my surprise they were very meaty indeed and I was able to draw a lorry load from them, and there will be another load in a fortnight's time.

Three weeks ago I had gone through the same sheep and scraped the barrel to get entries for the local carcase competition where, incidentally, I won no prizes. They killed out very well, though, but were not quite fat enough for the judges, who were I suspect old-fashioned in their tastes.

I sent some of this latest lot rather light but they were Hampshire and Dorset Down crosses and would have become overfat if kept much longer. All in all it's been a wonderful sheep year once lambing was over.

I should have started winter barley—Igri—when you read this. Not too bad a crop.

The wheat still looks well, all but Rapier has been sprayed for aphids. Is Rapier resistant to them?

But it has had to have a fungicide. I am still depressed about spring barley. The maltsters will have to cough up a big guarantee to make me grow more than I have to another year.

216

8th AUGUST

By August 18 my combines caught up with the ripening wheat and I stopped harvesting for a couple of days.

I had found that the standing crop was showing 23 per cent moisture even after a dry warm day.

There is no worse situation at harvest than to have the drier loaded with unripe wheat which will only pass through very slowly, meanwhile ripe grain is being piled up waiting to go through.

The main problem this year was that I was so depressed about harvest prospects that I never ordered the last conveyor to fill the latest store.

After all it was easily filled with the remnants of harvest last year and this year's crops did not look to be as good as they were then. But I was wrong.

Except for Triumph spring barley I have never known my grain yield better.

Igri started off with 52 cwt an acre as I said in my last article. Atem spring barley has averaged at just over 50 cwt whereas the Triumph only topped 2 tonnes in one field and to make matters worse has so much small grain that it won't be acceptable for malting.

The Atem has a good big berry and will be acceptable so long as the nitrogen level passes muster. As I don't know what a nitrogen level is or what it does there is nothing I can do to influence it, short of bribing the technician who determines these things.

He or she is probably incorruptible.

The amazing thing to me is that the old time maltsters, and millers too, produced perfect quality beers and bread without all these scientific tests which I believe have been introduced to force our prices down.

I don't think I shall grow Triumph again. This year it suffered both from mildew and brown rust while Atem stayed clean and green right through the season.

The drought of July was the last straw which sorted out the men from the boys in the plant world.

A lot of people tell me I am mad to persist with spring barley, but if you have the right variety such as Atem this year, which was my own seed by the way, it does not yield much worse than winter barley and there is always the chance of a malting sale.

It is also rather cheaper to grow, you don't have to spend so much money in over-time as you do when trying to cream it all into autumn drilling nor does it need so much nitrogen.

The real success this year has been the wheat. The 110 acres of Avalon produced 65 cwt an acre. Most of this was after peas or a two-year ley. But 14 acres following a succession of other cereals did not seem to be running any worse than the rest. No fungicides were used at all as it looked to be healthy but a late attack of aphids was sprayed out. Protein turned out to be 10.6 per cent.

I had been worried about Rapier which had suffered from drought. This has not yet been finished, but the first 50 acre block has averaged at least 62 cwt.

Part of this field had a fungicide because of a late attack of mildew but there were no aphids so none of the Rapier was sprayed for them. Is Rapier aphid-repellent? This by the way was second wheat.

I see no reason why the rest of the Rapier should not turn out as well on average. But my main hope is for about 50 acres of Maris Huntsman grown after oats which is still not ripe, but where the berry is bigger than I have ever seen it and does not seem to be shrivelling at all as it often does with this variety.

These are the best wheat crops for yield I have ever grown and most of the credit must go to the season, probably to the 4 in. of rain we had in late May and early June.

The only husbandry rule I stick to is that winter barley should not be sown until the last week in September and wheat sowing should not start before old Michaelmas, October 11.

1984 FARMING NEWS

Fishing Rules

I HAVE been thinking a lot over the past few weeks about the sad experience of a lady salmon fisher. For five years she had visited one of the better Welsh rivers, with absolutely no luck; then, on the last day of the season, she felt the magic double tug on her line. Eventually, and with some difficulty, she played the fish towards the shore.

The ghillie, who was watching from up the bank, came to land it for her, an offer she accepted gladly. But her gratitude soon turned to anger: for once the fish was in the net he turned to her and said it was foul-hooked in the dorsal fin and would, according to the rule book, have to be returned. He then proceeded to do just that.

A rational man would have thought that here, at least, were circumstances that justified a Nelsonian look at the rules.

Now, however, I am beginning to question my own initial aggressive reaction to this incident (had it happened to me, the ghillie probably would have followed the salmon into the stream). And I am starting to think that rules are there to be kept, even if they frustrate my killer instinct.

There was a time when my conscience was kept absolutely under control. I was never caught actually fishing a neighbour's water (I have extraordinary good eyesight) although I once had what I felt was a good precedent for deviating a bit from the strict boundary of my own beat. Coming round a corner of the River Test's bank, I found the neighbouring rod with the fly definitely in my water. He was a famous soldier and, seeing me, explained that his action was perfectly legal as long as his feet were in his beat. You do not argue with generals and he stumped off up the bank.

This last summer I found myself in the same situation. I had had a fruitless evening but there, just below my boundary, were two good, rising fish. I watched them a long time. I could have got below them, and in the gathering dusk no one would have seen me. Or, I could have let a fly float down from my own beat, as the general had been doing years before. Anyway, I let them go.

Then what about sticking to the presentation rules—that the

fly should always drop upstream? I must confess there have been times when, purely inadvertently the fly or nymph has drifted downstream and made a wide circle below the surface as I was winding it in. There have been occasions when it has been taken.

With my new-born purity of purpose I would now land it and, if it was sufficiently undamaged, return it carefully. A year or so ago I would have killed it straight away, and perhaps even boasted of the exploit. Not any more.

These sentiments have been nurtured, I suppose, by a general decline of the killer instinct latent in all of us, probably as a result of increasing age. I have come to the stage when I really want to outwit the fish without making it pay the supreme penalty.

Several people have written to me this year pointing out the advantages of using barbless hooks. I have done it myself inadvertently when the hook is of poor manufacture, and you notice it only when the fish drops off while being played. But even a barbless hook, while not injuring the mouth, can put great strain on the fish while being played.

If the real aim is to deceive the fish, why not simply cut off the bottom of the hook? Then, the fish has only to open its mouth to go free without damage.

January 1986   FINANCIAL TIMES

JOC had very little time for bankers. He used the down-to-earth style of the Farming News *column to air his views.*

Beware Bankers!

THE case of the Shropshire farmer suing his bank for wrong advice reminds me of an experience of my own, when I was young and very unused to the ways of this world.

I had just bought my first sizeable farm, and not having discussed it with my bank manager beforehand, went in to ask him for a bridging-loan so that I could go to the Agricultural Mortgage Corporation for a long-term loan at the going rate which was 3½ per cent.

'But my dear boy,' he said—he was that sort of bank manager—'you don't want to tie yourself up for 60 years or so at a fixed rate of interest. Now the bank will match the AMC, and you will have the flexibility of our varying rates of interest.'

Like a mug I fell for that one, with the result that when interest rates began to take off shortly afterwards, bank charges began to rise.

At 4 per cent I thought it was time to call a halt and moved over to the AMC where I have been ever since at their fixed rate set nearly 40 years ago of 4 per cent.

I then asked a solicitor if there would be any chance of winning a case against the bank for having persuaded me not to take the mortgage when I had the chance at 3½ per cent.

He did not think there was. I even went so far as to work out what ½ per cent on £25,000 over the next 58 years would be. It came to quite a lot of money for those days.

These days I suppose some sharp lawyer could probably make up a case on one of the share-the-profits arrangements they have in the USA.

But you should remember that the bank manager of those days commanded considerable respect.

He was believed to be the embodiment of financial probity and caution in the community. One just had to take his advice which was almost invariably of an ultra-conservative kind.

I think they meant very well by their clients, for it was considered really bad both for him and the reputation of the bank to have a farmer go wrong.

I remember Rex Paterson telling me 50 years ago that the local bank was refusing him an extension of his overdraft by £100. He went on to become one of Britain's biggest farmers.

A change came over the banking industry about 25 years ago. Its bosses realised that perhaps farming was not going to be let down and that the price of land which had just started to rise was going on its upward course. Had they not read in the papers that the city institutions were investing in land for long term capital growth and as a hedge against inflation? There would be money in it for banks and they set large numbers of keen young men looking for ways to share in this bonanza.

I have nothing at all against the specialists who have left the colleges and who, failing any opening into farming, have had to become bankers. After all with so many like myself continuing farming into their dotage there is nowhere else for them to go. But I wonder what their instructions were.

Were they told to find the best profits for the bank in the only way they could by increasing the amount of lending as a main priority? Did they sometimes overpersuade farmers to take up more money? I know of several farmers who were allowed to run up overdrafts which they had not a hope of ever paying off or even financing properly.

But the bank seemed to be quite happy to go on letting interest be added to the loan, secure in the knowledge that they would come out all right in the end.

It would be alright for the bank, but would it suit the farmer customer? I don't blame the banks a bit for looking after their own interests. But it is important to understand that they are money lenders pure and simple, whose primary interest is to make money for their employers.

Farmers should remember this when talking to a banker. It is not really fair to ask him for advice which in any case he probably has not the training to be able to give.

I read but really don't believe that some bankers charge a consultation fee. If, in fact, they do they should assume some responsibility for their advice.

You should remember that banks are also under a good deal of pressure these days. Not only have they loans to farmers on their books, they have lent enormous sums of money to some very doubtful overseas customers with very doubtful chances of ever getting it back.

They are going mad in the property market, buying up chains of estate agents so that they can be first in the queue when it comes to providing a mortgage to the lucky buyer.

There is a credit boom on now, and it is the main fuel of our high interest rates.

One of these days there will be a moment of truth. There will be a liquidity crisis and banks will have to call in their loans.

Already there are increasing numbers of defaulters in the house mortgage market. To survive banks will have to go to all sorts of measures to get some of their money back, to realise their collateral before it is too late and it loses too much of its value.

I NOTED with great interest a speech by Mr Robin Leigh-Pemberton in which he claimed that only 6 per cent of farmers made use of budgets and cash flows. Then he went on to claim that we were all a bunch of financial illiterates.

This coming from the governor of the Bank of England is pretty rich. The bank together with the Government is supposed to be responsible for the country's finances and after some eight years of Conservative rule has managed to present us with the highest interest rates in Europe.

As any traveller will know, the value of the £ as against other currencies fluctuates most disturbingly. One day it is up and on the next it is on the floor or looks like going there. There could be an advantage to us as farmers in a falling £ as it obviously is to industrialists who are always saying that the £ is overvalued. But we as farmers get the worst of all worlds because although we are cost-wise probably as efficient as any of our European neighbours, we cannot trade on fair terms with them because of the MCA system.

Some of Mr Leigh-Pemberton's remarks might of course have been addressed to the bankers themselves. What were they doing lending money to financial illiterates? When you think of the investment some banks have made in the farming sector, based presumably on the advice of their farming experts, one wonders if they had ever studied a farm cash flow either.

I thought it particularly poor banking when they based their lending on the asset value of the farm and not on the earning capacity.

Of course part of the trouble has been the way in which the British and other banks lent money to South America and other countries where the standard of financial responsibility is not very high. Much of this money was from the oil states and was simply lent on at higher interest rates. Now these countries are in trouble all round and we by high interest rates are making up for the stupidity of our bankers.

It is quite true that interest rates seem to be on the way down but that is not unconnected with the prospect of the election. Overall the country's balance of trade is not very promising. There could easily be a run on sterling and what better cure than a couple of per cent on the bank base as soon as Thatcher and Co are back in the saddle.

Thinking about this, there is a lot to be said for having an election every year, so that as soon as elected, politicians would have to start paying for next year's victory.

I do agree that farmers should budget as well as they can—in fact I do myself in my financially illiterate way—but it is far from being an exact science. I find that for climatic reasons alone there is a variation of at least 20 or 25 per cent in crop returns and very often a surge in unbudgeted costs. For instance, this spring I have had to resow some 20 acres of wheat and as well as that my large tractor which was budgeted to see me out packed it in and I had to lease another. I would have bought it outright had the initial allowances not been abolished.

IT won't have escaped your notice that all the big four banks have made provision for writing off some of their enormous loans to the third world.

None of these debtors are going to be turned out of their farms and homes as would-be debtors in this country.

Instead the shareholders of the banks will have to carry the can. So will all the rest of us whose bank charges will have to carry the burden of the banks' irresponsible lending.

I wonder how many of the members of the banks that made these loans are going to be given the sack for this lending.

For it was irresponsible as any visitor to some of these debtor nations could have told them at the time.

There is also a good case for anyone who is overborrowed now to claim third world status and ask for a remission of their borrowings.

I have been shown details of a number of farm borrowings recently and cannot understand how any farmer in his senses would take on such a load of debt. Nor do I understand how any prudent banker would lend the money.

It is of course true that some bankers simply looked at the capital value of the farm and estimated that if the worst happened and the farm had to be sold the bank would get its money back having allowed the interest to pile up into a capital sum.

Those bankers who relied on doing this deserved all the criticism which was made of them. That they are fearful of this criticism is shown by the fact that very few actual forced sales have come to light.

There are, I gather, some 10 per cent of us who are technically insolvent for whom I have the greatest sympathy.

It could be said of course that some of these borrowers were irresponsible. But surely a prudent banker would have felt it his duty to advise his client of the error of his ways and the doubt about the proposed enterprise.

A rough calculation on the back of an envelope would probably show how the land lay.

October 1986, May & August 1987   FARMING NEWS

Shooting

IN my early farming days I regarded myself as a member of the oppressed classes. I was a tenant and as such was not allowed the right to kill game, pheasants or partridges on the land I rented. I could, to protect my crops, shoot or trap rabbits or hares but the game was reserved for the landlord and his friends.

It was not that my landlords were particularly possessive but it frustrated me to see the birds eating my seed corn and to know that if I was tempted beyond endurance and did knock one off a row could follow. It was even worse if the shooting was let. Why should some city gent be able to get between me and a sport which I felt should belong to a real countryman?

Then I became a landowner myself of about 60 acres. This

completely altered the situation and also my attitude to those who used to indulge in a little illicit shooting on the land which I had acquired. I no longer joined in their depredations.

But it is one thing to own a bit of land and quite another to persuade birds to come onto it so that they can be legally shot. The rich can rear their own but those of us on their boundaries had to tempt them to cross the fences. In this I had an advantage because the pheasant and other game birds too are feral under the law. They belong to the land where they are at the time and as long as I had a game licence I could shoot them.

There are many ways of inducing pheasants to migrate. A chemist once gave me some oils with which I was to soak my boots and then walk through the neighbours' fields or down a lane where pheasants were known to dust themselves. According to him the birds would troop after me like suicidal lemmings. He must have got it out of a book because they never failed to do so. By careful feeding and the provision of a bit of cover I did manage to find something to shoot most days. But it was hard going and my neighbours' keepers used to run their dogs through my strip when I wasn't there.

By the time I became a sizeable landowner myself I was too accustomed to allowing others to do my game rearing for me. I reared none but continued my old habits only on a much bigger scale. By keeping my farm as a good game environment and not too heavily stocked, birds used to find their way there without special help. In this I was greatly helped by the mass rearing now indulged in by many shoots.

In the old days pheasants were hatched off and reared by broody hens. These brought up their chicks until they roosted and were often turned into the woods with them until they settled. It gave them a sense of home and they seldom wandered far. Those hatched in an incubator and then turned out into pens have no homing instinct as had the hen-reared birds.

There were of course wild birds as well and I used to have enough to have a few pleasant days rough shooting with a few friends, using dogs to move the game and taking it in turns to beat or stand. Quite a skilled operation really and one in which one has to work with nature.

I haven't shot a bird for a couple of years now and don't

really want to start again. In fact I don't like the noise and the smell of powder. It is not that I am against blood sports—it is just that I have lost the urge. But not altogether.

The other day I was on a farm where I used to enjoy my sort of shooting. It had all changed. There were beaters in uniform with flags, organisers with radio sets, marked posts for the guns to stand. The birds flew over fairly high and predictably, and busy ladies with dogs pick up the fallen. It was as well organised as a set piece battle, without an enemy to disrupt things.

I watched for a while and then the old instinct began to return. I could see an unwatched corner where a couple of cocks were stealing away. I saw too where a few strategic handfuls of grain scattered in a hedge bottom would tempt a few venturesome birds to leave home. If they were next door, I said to myself, I know how I would get them to come and visit me. Before I could allow myself to be tempted further I drove away.

November 1987   FINANCIAL TIMES

In all his years as a journalist, nothing stirred JOC more deeply than the Chernobyl disaster.

Chernobyl: Unanswered Questions

THE nuclear catastrophe at Chernobyl should be a warning to us all, that modern scientific techniques are not infallible and that accidents can happen no matter what political system they operate under. As witness the US space shuttle disaster, Three Mile Island, and even our own little local difficulties at Sellafield.

I am concerned both as a citizen and a farmer, and in these categories I am appalled at the lack of information provided by governments as to the possible dangers of radiation and the means of coping with them.

These dangers, it seems to me, are just as serious whether the radiation is a result of an act of war or of human inefficiency.

We are told that radiation is far more persistent than, say, poison gas; that it might take 40 years before the victims develop cancer; that it will be generations perhaps before genetic mutations appear in living animals and plants. It could be that governments do know what could happen and are fearful of the consequences of telling populations of the risks they are running either from nuclear weapons or nuclear power.

Some people are certainly getting the wind up. The EEC is forbidding the importation of foodstuffs from areas within 500 miles from Kiev. Even in Britain one is warned not to drink fresh rainwater in parts of the country—at least 1,000 miles from the accident site. We are told that the levels of radiation should cause no alarm. Then why send us to the tap or to bottled water?

In Germany and Holland farmers are advised to keep their cows indoors and not to sell their milk. In Russia one hears that livestock has had to be moved and that some land could be uncroppable for years. This may just be alarmist reaction, but in the absence of authoritative evidence, fantasy and rumour will flourish.

As a farmer, I think I should be told. As the crow flies, my farm is no more than 100 miles from Hinckley Point to the west, 150 miles from Sizewell and a little less than that from Dungeness, and say a couple of hundred miles from the nearest French reactor to the south. In any one of these an accident such as that at Chernobyl could happen.

I don't produce milk, but have large numbers of sheep and pigs which I am not able to put under cover. I can't even stop the sheep from drinking fresh rainwater as they get much moisture from wet grass. If livestock are affected, can they be killed for human consumption? How do I know how much they have been affected? And what about the crops? At this time of year growth is at its maximum. What damage will be done to them and to the land on which they are being grown? Are there any remedial steps that I can take?

These questions demand an answer—if there is a logical answer, that is. I would like to know what research is being done into the effects of radiation on plants and animals. There have been tales of secret tests which had some horrific results, but there has been no accurate information as to just how bad the results were. If there indeed have been these tests, farmers and the general public should know the risks they would be facing should there be a radiation accident, however caused.

In 1938–39 the British public was very apprehensive of war and air raids and gas as well. But as civilians we were trained in large numbers in air raid precautions which included protection against chemical warfare. Our instructors pulled no punches and we were told the facts from some pretty grisly diagrams. I don't know that the training would have been particularly effective if the worst happened, but at least we were trained to react. We knew what to expect.

I think it essential that we should be told the risks of atomic energy in relation to its benefits and if these risks are to be accepted then we should learn how to deal with the accidents when they happen.

May 1986   FINANCIAL TIMES

Chernobyl Conspiracy

I STILL believe that the most serious happening in farming recently was the Chernobyl disaster and I am appalled at the way the Government, aided by the NFU, is playing the catastrophe down.

I cannot understand why the NFU is not backing the CLA in calling for a full inquiry into the consequences of a similar accident, or even into the possible long-term effects of the Chernobyl fall-out.

It looks to me as if there has been a conspiracy to sweep the whole affair under the carpet in the interests of the nuclear industry to which the Government is deeply committed.

Then the NFU does not wish to see any bad publicity which might affect the sale of lambs from any hill areas.

I can understand the CLA's anxieties because already the sale of some of the farms in the affected areas has been made almost impossible.

No one wants to buy a farm on which part of the land will be contaminated for years to come.

In recent statements both Mr MacGregor and Peter Walker in Wales have said they are prepared to look again at the compensation.

But they have resolutely refused to agree to any real investigation of the overall lasting effects of radioactive fall-out.

But this should be the whole basis of such an enquiry. In my unscientific mind I equate radioactivity with the effects of strychnine which is a poison which kills again and again.

Apparently caesium has a half life of 30 years whatever that may mean. Will these restricted farms continue to be affected for 30 years or 300?

But the affected farms are only a small part of the whole problem. Chernobyl was a long way away. There are many power stations nearer in Europe and this country.

The chances of an accident happening increase with every addition of nuclear power.

Suppose that instead of the radioactivity falling in the underpopulated mountains, it fell in the intensively farmed areas.

It does not seem that we are at all prepared for such a happening. In the summer livestock would be out grazing, hay would be being made and silage as well. There are no published plans of what to do.

In Germany, Holland and Scandinavia, to say nothing of Eastern Europe, Chernobyl disrupted a whole summer's farming and marketing of milk.

I saw a report that intervention beef from the EEC sold to Venezuela turned out to be radioactive.

The cattle had been grazing last summer in Belgium and Denmark.

It may be that the effects of a nuclear accident are such that nothing sensible can be done about it. Or it could be that the Government does not wish to alert people to the dangers because it could spark off a demand for a phasing out of nuclear energy.

I believe that both as an industry and for the sake of the country, we should have an inquiry so that we could be prepared to deal with such an emergency should it arise. I would like to see some definite reason stated as to why this cannot be done.

The present policy of doing nothing is just getting us nowhere.

I have a special interest in this which you may think to be fanciful. I have long believed that mankind reached its present state before with nuclear power and all the rest and then an accident happened. This could have been a nuclear reaction and the world was just dissolved into its elemental parts.

Then after a suitable time man evolved once more from the primeval slime into the state where we now find ourselves where either stupid generals or equally stupid scientists seem to make it all happen again.

• • •

October 1987   FARMING NEWS

In the Wake of Chernobyl

From: Philip Butcher, The National Farmers' Union, London SW1

Sir—John Cherrington wonders (*Farming News*, October 23) why the NFU does not favour a public inquiry into the consequences for the UK of the Chernobyl disaster.

The answer is that we do not believe a public inquiry could bring out any information which is not already known. Knowledge is still very scanty about the behaviour of low-level radioactive fallout in the environment such as occurred in the wake of the Chernobyl explosion.

The NFU is satisfied that the Ministry of Agriculture has not attempted to hide anything. The Ministry itself is having to find out about the behaviour of the radioactive caesium which was brought down in the rain over the uplands of Cumbria, North Wales and South West Scotland in May 1986.

Ministry scientists have done a lot of patient experimental work over the past 15 months, and it is hoped that by the middle of next year this will enable them to predict with reasonable certainty when the contamination will have dropped below the threshold adopted for the restricted areas.

The threshold of 1000 becquerels per kilogram for lamb is of course a very low level which has been established to provide maximum safeguards for consumers. Similar or higher levels of contamination are derived by most people from their normal environment. The Government has sought to maintain public confidence in food as a first priority, and we entirely agree with this.

John Cherrington also discusses the implication of the Chernobyl experience for our national policy on nuclear energy.

This is a perfectly proper area of public debate, but is not a matter on which the NFU can take sides. We can only concern ourselves with nuclear energy issues insofar as these can be seen to pose a direct threat to farmers' interests.

October 1987   FARMING NEWS

Nuclear Bunglers

I JUST cannot accept the assurances from Mr Butcher's letter that the safety of farming from nuclear fallout from Chernobyl, or anywhere else, is safely in the hands of the Ministry of Agriculture and the NFU.

They did not even know until a week ago that the highest fallout from Chernobyl was in the Skipton area, although the Met Office had this information a year ago.

Why was this concealed?

Was it just due to inefficiency endemic in all bureaucracies?

As it happens there should be no trouble in collecting this sort of information. At the end of the last war I was in the Observer Corps and as I was leaving, it was being turned over to collecting nuclear fallout.

The posts were placed underground and the communications are still there.

With modern technology the whole thing could be made automatic and switched on should the need arise. The truth must be that the authorities who are sold on nuclear power are determined that it shall go ahead regardless.

I would have thought that the NFU would at least be insisting that provision should be made for nuclear accidents around the present power stations, where there is plenty of circumstantial evidence of an increase in radiation problems, leukemia and so on.

The Irish are very worried about this and claim that some fish stocks are contaminated. I am not so worried about the fish and animals but very much about human health.

Animals don't live very long, but according to general report it takes up to 40 years for radiation to kill humans.

Nor am I much impressed by those who say that even eating double or treble the number of becquerels will do no harm.

Has anyone yet been tested to destruction? I suggest that volunteers for this should come from the nuclear lobby or, if they should be a bit diffident, they could be conscripted. But seriously the NFU and the Ministry must look much more closely at the whole problem, because it won't go away.

November 1987 FARMING NEWS

The Two Johnnies Up the Creek Again

THE other morning I happened to hear Mr John Gummer holding forth in almost hysterical terms about how right the Government had been in its treatment of the Chernobyl fallout disaster.

I think he was speaking in Parliament and he told us he would be happy to eat meat at several times the becquerel count for ever and ever, confident that it would do him no harm.

Of course, politicians are notably thick-skinned and no doubt he was confident that his guts were as tough as his hide undoubtedly is. But why is it that there is such a conspiracy of silence?

I was sorry too to see that some of the Cumbria NFU are talking of suing those who are making such a fuss, on the grounds that it was spoiling the sale of their mule lambs. A very selfish attitude which could well rebound on them one day.

My main interest in this is not Chernobyl or the threat of a nuclear war, but to highlight the fact that the Ministry has, so far as I know, made no plans at all for farms or people to be protected in the event of nuclear fall-out from another accident.

Why has the Ministry been so remiss, about this? I can only conclude that it is under the strictest orders from the nuclear-generating lobby, led by the Prime Minister, which is determined that whatever happens, the nuclear age has come to stay.

• • •

December 1987   FARMING NEWS

Can We Believe?

THE release of the secret documents of 1957 under the 30 year rule which showed that Macmillan as Prime Minister concealed the real facts of the Windscale disaster just underlines the dangers of believing Government statements.

How do we know with this precedent if we have been told the truth about the Chernobyl fall-out? I just do not believe a word either the Government spokesmen or their NFU supporters have had to say on the subject.

Nuclear power will be the basis of our energy policy and nothing like the truth is to be allowed to raise doubts in people's minds which might cause them to fail to subscribe to the shares of the electricity industry if and when it should be privatised.

• • •

According to an article in the *Independent* of January 4, the fall-out of this disaster reached the USA in May 1986, where it

234

seems to have affected milk supplies to some extent.

What is really significant is that deaths from all causes in the US rose by 30,000 for that summer. The causes are not yet analysed but the statistical link is clear.

Not all those affected died of cancer of course, but I wonder how many premature deaths in the Sellafield area over the past 30 years were caused by the accident, and I wonder too how many will happen after the Chernobyl accident. I simply cannot understand why the National Farmers' Union is backing the Ministry in refusing a full-scale inquiry unless they think that if the findings come out the wrong way so far as they are concerned they may lose property values.

• • •

January 1988   FARMING NEWS

By January 1988 JOC was seriously ill and confined to the farmhouse at Tangley. He continued to write, however, with the same keen insight and humour. The Financial Times *introduced him to the Tandy—a computer terminal whose technology he mastered with consummate ease and enthusiasm.*

Pigs and Sydney

WHEN I took to farming many years ago a wise farmer told me that even if I kept a herd of pigs for 50 years they would neither bankrupt me nor make me rich. Most of the time, he said, they would do just well enough to stop me selling them.

After devoting my best efforts to the problem for more years than I care to remember I am bound to confess that he was right.

My pig farming apprenticeship began as a young student on a Danish farm, of which my main memory is of constant hard work in cold weather. The closest I was allowed to the secrets of Danish pig farming was to clean out the sties on Sunday mornings. Then as now Denmark's pig farming was recognised as representing the state of the art, but little can be learnt about balanced rations and their formulation from the tines of a dung fork.

I eventually started my own herd, using the best stock then available, and contracted my output to the old Pigs Marketing Board.

I soon discovered that however well bred the parent stock was there was no guarantee that their progeny would match up to them. I should have known this of course, because there are a whole lot of environmental factors which affect production, such as temperature and feed quality. There are also different genes within each family of a species and they react differently.

There was, however, another and much more fundamental difference between me and my Danish counterparts.

The Danish farmer of those days was a disciplined and loyal co-operator. He obeyed the grading rules laid down by his co-operative factory, even if they went against him. After all, he had little option. All stock went through the export bottleneck and that which failed to pass was sold on the local market and received a much lower price.

It was not the same in Britain. There always was a good fresh pork market and prices on this were frequently above those for bacon pigs. Dealers would call round the farms making tempting offers which were difficult to resist. What infuriated some of us was to find that these same dealers were supplying the bacon factories at prices which were higher than those on our contracts.

In the end an outbreak of swine fever enabled me to sell out the pigs and at the same time I moved to another farm, where there were no pig buildings. So I was able to cancel my contract with the Pigs Marketing Board with a fairly clear conscience.

Conscience should not really enter into it at all. There

is nothing sacrosanct about the co-operative principle which is held up to us as the ideal to aspire to. It suited the small farmers of Denmark, the Netherlands and other places to band together to attack particular markets collectively. And it suited them sometimes to impose some pretty stiff sanctions against the unco-operative just to make them conform.

I went back again into pigs in a fairly big way some 25 years ago. These were not baconers but what might be called general purpose pigs mainly for the fresh pork trade. They were all graded under the rules of the Meat and Livestock Commission. I was paid on the grading results and conformed with the rules.

I had good breeding stock and used artificial insemination to secure the best results, but things did not turn out too well in the grading. It seemed that however carefully the parents were chosen there were big differences in the way in which the carcases of the offspring graded.

A great deal depends on the thickness of the shoulder fat and carcase grading, as far as British pigs are concerned, is still in its infancy.

There is no doubt though that over the last few years the demand for lean British pigs has expanded enormously and pork is the fastest growing meat product on the market, after chicken. But once again history seems to be repeating itself. Those doing best out of the pig market have been those who sell their pigs on the open market without grading. There is always a marginal demand for supplies, and buyers who are short cannot worry about a little matter like quality grading. Of course success in this depends on there always being a marginal shortage.

Margins became very bad a couple of years ago, however, and I decided to run down the herd. If I had been younger and had the capital available I would have put in a more modern set up. In fact I retained the nucleus of my breeding stock so that I could be in business again within a short time. But I believe British pig breeding is on the wrong lines these days. The Europeans are using a general purpose pig which can be tailored to fit whatever market suits it at the time. There seems to be no need for specialised grading as for our pork or bacon pigs. It all looks as though it will be much easier in future.

For my part I still have an interest in pigs, or rather in

one pig. He is quite the ideal animal, needing no feeding and making no mess. He is house-trained and lives in the sitting room watching the TV, especially the snooker. And as he is immortal he will never be subject to grading.

He came about like this.

James, a local sculptor, asked if he could carve some of my pieces of elm into the shapes of farm animals. I sketched what I thought was the ideal pig shape for modern demands and told him to carry on. I told myself that with this model always before me I would have something to go on when the need arose.

It did not work out like that at all. James produced three pigs. One we would call a runt, hairy, with a squashed up nose. Another sat upright with a flat snout for holding a glass. The third was Sydney, whose likeness accompanies this article.

'This is not what I showed you,' I complained. 'But this is how I saw them,' came the reply. An artist, I was told, did not work to orders like a photographer.

I took to Sydney in the end. His stuck up ears resemble nothing so much as the roofs of the Sydney Opera House, hence the name. And in his shape he has every characteristic, good and bad, of every pig I have ever owned. The only attention he requires is a gentle massage with a dab of Cherry Brandy, which seems to give him a rosy glow.

He is, in fact, the ideal household pet. I wish that I had met him 50 years ago—it would have saved me a lot of money and effort.

January 1988 FINANCIAL TIMES

Surviving the Bad Times

ONLY a few years ago, when he was Minister of Agriculture, Mr Peter Walker was advising British farmers to increase their production so as to save imports of food. This was nonsensical advice at a time when all farm produce exporters were increasing their output, including fellow members of the European Community.

Equally ill-advised were the sizeable grants available then from the Farm and Horticultural Development Scheme which tempted many farmers to borrow more than they should have done in order to put expansion schemes into operation. They are rueing the consequences now.

Being an old fashioned peasant type I borrowed no money in that period and only invested in new capital works when the initial allowances were 100 per cent. Now my policy is to lease equipment and eventually I shall own nothing but a heap of scrap iron. But I should at least be solvent.

Most other serious problems faced now by British farmers are connected with membership of the EC. I was always against joining on the terms offered, and because I said so in print, I used to be told that it would be much easier to negotiate the right terms once inside than from the outside. That view has not been borne out by experience.

The present row over measures to contain EC farm support spending through budget 'stabilisers' and/or cereal acreage set-asides is a case in point. Apart from the Dutch there appears to be general support for the set-aside approach. But while the others also want a degree of price maintenance for what is produced above the target level the UK negotiators want set-asides to be backed up by a price reduction.

The British justify their case for price cuts by pointing to the much lower levels ruling on the world market. These prices, however, are not really 'world prices'—they are set by the US Export Enhancement Program. A US wheat farmer can take advantage of a deficiency payment which brings his wheat price to just above $4 a bushel, equivalent to just under £100 a tonne—a figure we British could probably live with.

The only countries which are paying their farmers the world free market price are Australia and Argentina and both of those are reducing production.

It is probable that the real cost of growing and marketing grain is roughly the same in terms of resources used wherever it is grown, something Britain's fellow EC members are well aware of.

In fact there is quite a degree of optimism about the future of grain trade. It started at conferences in the UK and in Europe and spread to the US Wheat Associates meeting in New Orleans recently, where an observer told me that he was particularly impressed by the attitude of the main shippers, who prophesied a wheat shortage by the autumn.

That attitude has been taken up by British farmers who, in spite of ministerial warnings, do not seem to be taking much notice of the present set-aside proposals. At a recent grain growers' conference one speaker pointed out that by the year 2000 there would be, on current projections, another 1bn mouths to feed worldwide and argued that there would be demand for all the grain farmers could grow.

What has got British farmers really angry has been the 'Green Pound Syndrome'. The green pound—the artificial exchange rate used to translate EC support prices into sterling—is at present so overvalued as to reduce the earning power of every acre of UK farm land by about £25. That assessment is based on Lord Northampton's estate, where unless something is done a number of tenants could go bankrupt and others give up farming.

The National Farmers' Union and other bodies are submitting similar arguments, but so far the British Government has refused to do anything about it, and until we join the European Monetary System I fear nothing will be done.

At the moment this suits the Government because it keeps consumer food prices down.

Farmers might feel less aggrieved if the Government explained in simple terms why the disparities existed and what could be done about them. Sir Geoffrey Howe was asked about this the other day and simply said that British farmers had their advantages—but he did not try to specify them.

As a recently failed pig farmer—defeated by the subsidy on

Dutch and Danish bacon imports resulting from green currency distortions—I am feeling very sore indeed, although I should have known better than to expect fair play as we know it from the Europeans.

I could of course export my grain to the Netherlands, but unfortunately there is a little matter of about a £20 a tonne levy against it.

And now, just to confuse the picture further, Mr John North of the department of land economy at Cambridge University is telling us that by 1992 we shall have to take 30 per cent of productive land out of farming just to make up for the 2.5 per cent increase in productivity to be expected by then.

Farmers are baffled, but a consultant of my acquaintance says he has the answers.

First he looks at the rent. If there is a landlord he tells the tenant to get it halved for a start. There is no reason, he suggests, why landlords, who have had a good run lately, should not share the general grief. Does the tenant think anyone else would pay any more?

If the 'rent' is a finance charge then assets can be sold and second-hand or hired machinery used. It may be somewhat less efficient but the exercise could still turn small losses into small profits.

Next comes the labour force.

'What does that old chap do for his 50 quid a week?' he asks.

'Well, he rears a few calves and does a little gardening,' replies the farmer.

'Could your wife not rear the calves? Or could she bring in the money in any other way?'

Then there are the two men looking after 120 cows and followers at a cost of about £20,000 a year.

'There is big scope here for a saving,' says the consultant triumphantly.

'But how?' the client asks with a sinking heart.

'Well if you really wish to go on farming you will milk the cows yourself and your wife will see to the calves . . . What do you do any way?'

'Well I go to market and manage things generally,' says the farmer. 'But what that means is difficult to say. In any case in 30 years of farming I have never done any practical farm work.'

The consultant is not impressed. 'If you wish to survive the present difficulties you will never learn younger, if you don't . . . good afternoon.'

February 1988   FINANCIAL TIMES

JOC died on 19 February 1988.

Index